D0440029

HARRY IS A LIAR!

Don't believe a word uttered by fat Harry Mudd
the space rogue—it will get you into dangerous
trouble! Spock, Scott and McCoy understand that
as they confront the inspired absurdities of the
obscenely overweight Mudd, *aka* Captain Leo
Walsh, captain of a space ship. Yet they voyage
to strange adventures in a dazzling and mysterious intragalactic thriller known as . . .

MUDD'S ANGELS
A Star Trek Novel

- The adventure of the frantic fat man and the
  wilting beauties
- The illegal and incredible Venus Drug
- Rigel 12—a no-man's-land of a planet where
  they mine the most precious substance in the
  galaxy—dilithium

MUDD'S ANGELS

ADAPTED BY J. A. LAWRENCE

MUDD'S ANGELS
A Bantam Book | May 1978

ISBN 0-553-11802-1

Published simultaneously in the United States and Canada

Bantam Books are published by Bantam Books, Inc. Its trade-
mark, consisting of the words "Bantam Books" and the por-
trayal of a bantam, is registered in the United States Patent
Office and in other countries. Marca Registrada. Bantam
Books, Inc., 666 Fifth Avenue, New York, New York 10019.

PRINTED IN THE UNITED STATES OF AMERICA

*Dedicated to the
Memory of
James Blish*

INTRODUCTION

THIS BOOK COMPRISES the fourteenth and last of the first three seasons' presentations of the live *Star Trek* series. The first two sections, *Mudd's Women* and *I, Mudd*, by Stephen Kandel, were first telecast in 1966 and 1967; the third section, *The Business, as Usual, During Altercations*, was written for this book by J.A. Lawrence.

James Blish, the adapter of the other scripts in the series, died in 1975. He left part of *Star Trek 12*, and the two Kandel scripts above, partially completed. They have been given a little polishing by J.A. Lawrence in the course of preparing these two books for publication.

Please note that, due to a Tholian Web of great complexity having to do with rights and agreements, it was necessary to disregard the episode referring to Harry Mudd from the animated series.

Again, thank you all for your letters. They do keep coming; the way *Star Trek* lives is a miracle.

I would like to thank Mr. Dennis Simopoulos,

Director of the Astronomy Department of the Eugenides Institute, for his technical help and endless patience.

May the Great Bird of the Galaxy watch over us all.

J.A. Lawrence
Athens
1977

For those of you who ask how to get in touch with *Star Trek* groups, you can write to the *Star Trek* Welcomittee, P.O. Box 206, New Rochelle, New York 10804, for a directory. They ask that you send a stamped, self-addressed envelope when requesting information. The Welcomittee Central Information Center is c/o Mary Louise Dodge, P.O. Box 207, Saranac, Missouri 48881.

PROLOGUE

ONCE THE MUDD affair was straightened out for good and all—insofar as anyone can be sure it *was* straightened out—the Scientific Advisory Board demanded an explanation of it, and Starfleet Command so ordered us. Few orders I have ever received turned out to be so difficult, but with the aid of my officers I managed to put one together.

The report now lies in the SAB's immense library computer, and may be read by any authorized person, but it is dull stuff, as such reports have to be. It leans heavily on the facts, and the facts are the least illuminating part of the Mudd affair. What mattered was the man, and the SAB is relentlessly impersonal.

When I had put the wooden document into final form as best I could, and Lieutenant Uhura had transmitted it to Command, I said so. I do not recall my exact words, but I think I said, "The Board won't get anything out of that, and nobody else will ever read it."

"Too true," said Mr. Scott, my Engineering Officer. "It was aye a crazy business from start to finish, and muckle glad I am that we're shut of it. But yon report drains all the life out o't."

I tried to catch the eye of my Chief Medical Officer, Dr. Leonard McCoy, but he was looking glumly at the deck. "Bones?" I said. "What do you think?"

"I suppose Scotty's right," McCoy said, rather reluctantly. "Of course we did include my psychological analysis of Mudd, but there's not much feeling in that either. Nothing knocks down an experience like trying to stuff it into the SAB's pigeonholes."

"Well, that's that, anyhow," I said. "Too bad we couldn't give it any of the flavor, but we had no choice. Do you agree. Mister Spock?"

My First Officer, who is half Vulcan, is notorious in Star Fleet for his devotion to facts and logic (though too few people know as much as we do about his more important courage, honor and loyalty). Aboard the *Enterprise,* Dr. McCoy, who knows better, pretends he thinks Spock a sort of organic computer. Even I was surprised when Spock said:

"Not entirely, Captain. A better account might be possible, and if so, I would think it desirable."

"Oho. Please tell us why."

"The Mudd business—or the series—occurred in a reasonably well-organized area of the galaxy, Captain; an area where law and order either prevailed, or could be expected to prevail in the near future. The Scientific Advisory Board obviously believes that a detailed description of the events will make matters run more smoothly still.

"I am not so sanguine. Mudd was a random factor, a human sport who misbehaved and upset all calculations. He was a fascinating aberration, and I think it likely that he will not be the last. The Board, safe at Headquarters, has forgotten that such wild offshoots ever happened, and might happen again. Nor can we so remind them, for the form in which we were required to report precludes it. It would perhaps be well to make a closer record, in language that someone else might read, as a general warning that human beings can be wildly erratic."

"Not, of course, including you," McCoy said.

"Bones, belay that—Mister Spock's human side has saved us all time and and time again!"

"I know that. Sorry, habit dies hard. Spock, apologies."

"Accepted, Doctor."

"But what can we do?" I asked the bridge in general. "Lieutenant Uhura, you're our Communications Officer. Could you make a proper tale of the Mudd affair—make people understand the craziness Scotty mentioned, the problem Mister Spock sees in it, the way we felt about it? I agree that it would be worth doing."

"Captain, I doubt it," she said, giving me my second surprise in as many minutes; the skills involved in her specialty were so various that I'd been sure they included this one. She must have seen my reaction. "You see, sir, my job is to communicate facts—or sometimes to conceal or distort them, but telling a long, complicated story—and this one is surely complicated!—is a special talent, and people who have it usually *aren't* encouraged to go into Communications. No captain wants a Communications Officer with an irresistible urge to romancing, or embroidering the truth when he finds it dull."

"We don't need embroidering to this tale, but I take your meaning. Are we stymied, then? Or do you have an alternative idea?"

"I do. Our civilian passenger—"

"Lawrence? The Integrator? Surely they aren't encouraged to romance, either."

"No, Captain, but an Integrator nevertheless does more than merely observe and record events. He has to weigh them for relative importance, draw inferences and make interpretations.

"What I suggest is that all of us draw up our

own individual accounts of our encounters with Mudd, including the computer. Then we hand the documents to Integrator Lawrence to . . . integrate as a narrative."

"A splendid idea," I said. "But would the Integrator do it? I have no power to issue orders to civilians, except where the survival of the ship or the mission is concerned."

"I think so. It will probably be quite a while before we reach Alpha Aldiss, and I don't suppose there's much to integrate before we arrive. I think Lawrence might be persuaded." She smiled. I did too—Uhura can be very persuasive.

"Mister Spock, gentlemen, your opinions?"

There were no demurrers, and Integrator Lawrence, it turned out, needed no persuasion. What follows, then, is that story. We are still too close to the events it covers to know how much sense it will make to a fresh mind. We are, however, quite sure that it is more coherent than anything we could have produced.

James T. Kirk
Captain
U.S.S. *Enterprise*
Star date 6107

PART I

MUDD'S WOMEN
by
Stephen Kandel

STAR DATE 1329.1

CLEARLY, the moving light on the *Enterprise* screen was not a star. Stars do not adopt evasive tactics. They do not try to run away from starships, but stay put in their orbits. So the moving light on the screen was baffling. Captain James T. Kirk frowned at it.

"An Earth vessel, Mister Spock?"

"It's hard to say, Captain. I'm getting no registry beam from it."

Chief Engineer Scott halted in his rounds of the bridge stations to look at the screen. "If that *is* an Earth vessel, he'll be overloading his engines in a minute."

The moving light changed course. They watched the maneuver in silence. Then Sulu said from his console, "He knows we're after him, Captain!"

"Stay with him." Kirk got up from his command chair to go to the Communications console, but Lieutenant Uhura shook her head. "I've tried all frequencies, sir. He either refuses to answer, or he's not reading us."

Its changed course was heading the odd light into the dense glitter of an asteroid group. Kirk's frown deepened. "Deflectors on, Mister Farrell."

The red-headed navigator, hitting a control, evoked the hum of the deflector screens. Sulu said sharply, "He's seen the asteroids, sir."

Kirk nodded. "We remain with him, Mister Farrell. He's trying to lose us among them."

Spock called, "Captain, I make it out as Earth vessel composition about the size of the small J-class cargo ships——" He broke off as his sensors gave him new, alarming news. "His engines are super-heating!"

Farrell shouted, "There go the engines now, sir!"

Kirk wheeled toward the screen. The light had burst into a flare—and winked out. Darkened and now powerless, the small vessel would be drifting at the mercy of the speeding asteroids. A somber Farrell said, "He's had it. One impact, and that'll be one dead ship. Unless—we could put our deflector screens around him—?"

Scott, his mind on his precious engines, cried, "We'll overload ourselves if we try that, Captain! He's too far away!"

Kirk ignored him. "Mister Farrell, cover him with our deflector screen. Mister Scott, Mister Spock—stand by in the Transporter Room."

The hum of the screen rose high and strained. To the flash of red lights the alarm whined through the bridge. At his own console, Kirk was close to regretting his decision. Engine temperature was climbing, far too rapidly. The needle rose higher . . . higher.

The lights dimmed and brightened. "That, sir, was one of our dilithium circuits," said Sulu.

Kirk seized his intercom. "Bridge to Transporter Room. Start beaming that crew aboard!"

The lights dimmed again. Uhura, over the protesting roar of the engines, cried, "I'm getting a distress signal from them, sir!"

Kirk spoke into his mike. "We're getting a response, Mister Scott. Ask them for coordinates."

"I have, sir. We're locking on!"

Medikit in hand, McCoy hurried to the Transporter Room. But the materialization process taking place on the platform startled him. Though all the six positions on the platform were activated, only one shape was gathering substance. It gathered a lot of it. It continued to collect it for some time, until it had formed into an obscenely fat man. He wore a shabby, gilt-buttoned uniform of no known designation and a yachting cap was set rakishly on a gray, curly fringe of greasy hair. But despite the soft jowls that spilled over the collar of his uniform, McCoy did not think he looked soft. He had the unmistakable air of a man who knows his way around—and has often been around it. With an unconvincing look of narrow-eyed suspicion, he stepped from the platform.

"Not meaning ingratitude," he said, "but where is it I find myself?"

McCoy, replacing his kit, said, "On board the U.S.S. *Enterprise*."

The fat man glanced heavenward. "Praise be." He extended a pudgy hand to the doctor. "I am Walsh—Captain Leo Walsh."

McCoy ignored the hand. Spock pressed forward. "How many more in your crew?"

Yellow teeth showed in a grin. "Just a few more."

Scott said, staring, "Your vessel's breaking up, man! If we don't get them over here *now* . . ."

"Wasn't sure this was a friendly ship." Walsh pointed to the Transporter controls. "All three of 'em should be in position now."

Scott swept his hand down across the console.

Up on the bridge, the lights dimmed again and did not brighten. Kirk saw the third dilithium circuit indicator cease to function.

"We're supplementing with battery power, sir," said Sulu worriedly.

"Mister Scott! Are they all on board yet?" said Kirk into the mike.

"Only one, sir. But we're locked on to three more."

"There she goes!" yelled Farrell.

The screen flashed as an asteroid hit the darkened ship in dead center. Then the bland, oblivious stars returned. If any human life had been aboard . . . "Are they safe, Scotty? Did you get those others?"

"I—I can't say, sir."

Scott, like McCoy and Spock, was anxiously watching the transporter platform. It glittered with the sparkles that preceded materialization, but that was all. McCoy glanced at Walsh. Though some concern showed on his fat face, he stood composedly, almost nonchalant; a man on intimate terms with that unpredictable female, Lady Luck.

Urgently, Kirk's voice reached them. "Their ship's gone. *Did you get those three, Mister Scott?*"

"We're not sure, sir. We're locked on to *something.*"

McCoy went to the console. "Scotty, what's wrong?"

"I dinna ken! With the dilithium crystals out—"

"At best," Spock said, "it will take longer on battery power."

"Never trusted the blasted thing anyway," McCoy growled. "Dematerializing people, squirting their atoms around the universe like—"

"*Now!*" said Spock. "Got them!"

The shimmering on the platform was assuming shapes—shapes that pulled a gasp from Scott. Three women slowly coalesced—three women, each possessed of a loveliness calculated to fire ardor in the breasts of saints. All the words occurred to McCoy . . . "captivating" . . . "breathtaking" . . . "gorgeous." A blonde of golden dreams; a dark enchantress who might have launched the Greek armada toward Troy; a small, silvery nymph who suggested ice lit by fire within. And their appeal was frankly sexual. They smiled in open invitation to every man in the room.

Even Spock was taken aback. Scott whispered, "How about that?"

Walsh went to the platform. "It's all right, ladies. We're in good hands."

Good or bad, they intended to be in somebody's hands at the first opportunity. They made this abundantly lucid by the way they moved from the platform.

Still ignorant, up on the bridge, of the kind of guests he was entertaining, Kirk signaled the Transporter Room. There was no reply. Farrell, turning, said, "We're clearing the asteroid belt now, Captain."

"Deflector screen off. Conserve power, Mister Farrell."

As the whine of the strained engines diminished, Kirk tried the Transporter Room once more. "Are you reading me or not, Mister Scott?"

Spock's troubles began as he escorted the group down the corridor. Within three minutes he counted twenty dropped jaws as crewmen forgot why they had been passing. The women swayed, deliberately provocative, highly subversive. As he herded them into the elevator, he drew a deep breath of relief.

Walsh undertook to enlighten him. "These starships are somethin'—but men are men, wherever they are. Machinery will never take it out of 'em."

Spock addressed the elevator's control console. "Deck Twelve."

Walsh glanced at his ears. "You're part Vulcan?"

Spock nodded, eyeing him calmly. Mudd whistled, silently. "So a pretty face doesn't affect you? Not unless you want it to."

It was an unfortunate remark. The women closed in around him, drawn like magnets to the lodestone of the unattainable. It was not the first time that Spock had encountered this phenomenon; he gently but firmly interposed a lever between himself and the women.

"Save it, ladies," said Walsh with a careless shrug. "This breed can switch off its feelings."

Spock's eyes flicked him, but his face was impassive. The dark girl spoke. "I apologize for Mister Walsh, sir. He's so used to buying and selling people, he—"

"*I'll* handle the conversation, love," Walsh told her.

On the way to the Captain's cabin, the men who didn't stop to gape indulged themselves in appreciative whistles: discipline on the *Enterprise* appeared to be seriously threatened. Stalking ahead of the guests, Spock very sincerely wished that Walsh's vessel *had* been a J-class cargo ship.

Kirk's back was turned as he ushered the party into the cabin, which had not been designed for the comfort of six people. Spock's left eyebrow cocked in well-controlled amusement. He'd set up this encounter, and was mildly curious to see the results. He spoke in his most formal military tone.

"The commander of the transport to see you, sir."

The fuming Kirk wheeled. "What the . . . hell did you think you were doing?" is what he had meant to say. He never said it.

The wave of female magnetism hit him like a blow; the three beautiful women liked what they saw, and he was going to like them. Long eyelashes swept up and down over gleaming eyes. Hips rolled sweetly in the close quarters; Spock would have sworn he could smell musk. They liked the Captain; they liked his looks, they liked his bad temper, they liked the set of his shoulders—and above all, they liked the way he was looking at them. Walsh, wearing an affable, knowing smile, let Nature take its course.

Kirk groped for his lost composure. "And— these ladies? Are they your . . . your crew, Commander?"

The fat man showed yellow teeth in a grin. "No, Captain. They're my cargo."

Kirk swallowed. He looked at the women. *Cargo?* These divinities of female shape? That somber beauty—the heat was too much. He ran a finger round the suddenly-tight collar of his shirt. He dragged his eyes to the unpleasantness of Mudd.

"Uh—what do you mean by *cargo?*"

"The ladies are cargo. Cargo is my business. However, if your question concerns the character of these ladies, let me assure you—"

"My business is with you!" Kirk snapped. "See to the ladies, Mister Spock." He nodded to the women, again feeling the palpable wave of attraction. "If you'll follow my First Officer—"

"I detect a note of Puritanism in you, Captain," said Walsh. "Not uncommon in lonely ship captains." He grinned again. "You can rest easy. I absolutely guarantee the purity, the virtue, the high moral standards of these delicious—"

"Thank you, Mister! So noted!" said Kirk with ill-suppressed fury. He turned to the ladies. "If you'll follow my First Officer—"

"Captain." The voice was lustrous and low. The planes of her cheeks gave her wide eyes the hint of a slant. A faint rose flush colored her golden face as she looked deep into Kirk's eyes.

"I'm Eve," she said. "And we'd much rather stay." Her smile was intimate—meant for him alone. The sudden dimples that showed briefly promised laughter and joy—just for him. He swallowed.

Spock came to his rescue. He opened the cabin door, saying, "This way, please, ladies . . ."

What was it about her eyes that wouldn't let his go? Kirk was faintly aware that Walsh was enjoying his struggle. Spock, urging the women through the door, raised an eyebrow, and Kirk found himself released—and angry.

Walsh, with one last satisfied glance at the closed door, turned briskly, forestalling Kirk's first question. "Well, Captain, how could I know this was a starship—me with a cargo of lovelies aboard? A strange vessel looms up; naturally I tried to evade you."

Kirk waited. Let the fat man say his piece.

"Starship captain or no, you exceeded your rights, chasing me and mine into an asteroid shower!" said Walsh.

"Your name, please," said Kirk.

"Walsh. Leo Walsh. And you cost me my vessel. It—"

"Mister Walsh, I'm convening a ship's hearing on your actions. Mister Spock will supply you with any legal information you require for your defense. That will be all, sir."

Walsh shook his head sadly. "You're a hard-nosed one, Captain."

"And you're a liar, Mister Walsh. I think we both understand each other." He spoke into the intercom. "Security!"

When the guard appeared, Kirk said, "Escort Mister Walsh to quarters. He's to remain confined."

Walsh strolled after the guard, his bearing that of a man who has not yet summoned all his arcane resources—resources far beyond the grasp of a simple starship captain.

. . . So her name was Eve. A name that had meant trouble from the beginning, and looked as if it had every intention of continuing. He rubbed his cheek. A shave; that's what he needed. A shave and some time to sort out the disturbing implications of this situation.

Spock had seen the disturbing elements to their cabin. He was supervising the bridge when

Sulu and Farrell emerged from the elevator. Farrell stumbled as he went toward this station, looking utterly dazed.

Sulu caught his arm, and snapping his fingers in front of Farrell's eyes, said, "You're on duty, Johnny-o. Back to reality."

Farrell tumbled into his chair. "You can *feel* their eyes when they look at you. Like something grabbing hold of you. You notice that?" Farrell looked at Sulu, and at his console, seeing neither.

"I noticed," nodded Sulu. *"How* I noticed."

Spock eyed them curiously as they settled into position. The mating instinct of human beings was a rather unattractive mystery . . . and extraordinarily obsessive.

"We've got trouble, Mister Spock." Scott's voice was low and urgent. "One dilithium crystal left —and it's got a hairline split at the base."

"Rig a bypass circuit, Mister Scott."

"I can't, sir. We blew the whole converter assembly."

Spock looked up sharply; this was likely to be serious. He opened the intercom to the Captain's cabin. "Spock here, Captain. You're needed on the bridge."

The guard in the Briefing Room was doing his best not to look at the three graces who sat at the table. It was the most difficult assignment of his life to date. But he held his ground when Walsh, entering with some stained papers in his hand, said, "Mind waiting outside, buddy boy?"

The guard didn't like being addressed as "buddy boy" to start with, and he had his orders, "Sorry, sir."

Walsh hesitated. Then, joining the women, he spoke to them carefully. "The three of you, answer any questions you're asked. Don't lie—you don't have to. And don't submit to a—" He glanced at the guard. "Being healthy, you don't need a medical exam, do you, girls?"

The guard thought privately that nothing so

glowing could be unhealthy. Seemed silly to be making such a point of it.

The women nodded. "But what if they ask us about—" said the blonde sprite in the pale blue and silver tunic.

"They won't," Walsh said hastily. He turned toward the guard again. "Don't you have some place to go, lad?"

He'd not be off duty for another hour. He stood his ground.

The smoky dark girl said tensely, "They'll notice. They'll notice we're dif—"

Walsh whirled, cutting her off. "They won't. Leave the answering to me, Ruthie—all of you, loves. We'll get—"

Eve said, *"Where* will we get? We don't have a ship, we're heading the wrong way, Harry . . ."

"Sst!" Walsh hissed. "Leo—Leo Walsh!" He remarked loudly to the guard, "They're lovely, aren't they, lad? As long as they think lovely and smile . . . they'll come out on top somewhichway, right?" He stood so the girls could see his face, but the guard could not. "My promise on it!" The women settled back—Walsh's yellow smile took in both guard and girls.

Kirk entered the bridge at a run.

"The entire ship's power is feeding through one crystal, sir." Spock was grave.

"Then we switch to bypass circuits."

"They burned out when we superheated, Captain. That jackass Walsh not only wrecked his own vessel, but in saving his skin we—"

"If it makes you feel any better, Mister Scott, that's one jackass we're going to see skinned," said Kirk.

"It's frustrating, sir. Almost a million gross tons of vessel depending on a hunk of crystal the size of my fist," grumbled the engineer.

Spock said, "And that crystal won't last long —not pulling all our power through it." He paused. "One alternative possibility, Captain.

There is a lithium mining operation on Rigel Twelve—high-grade ore, I've heard."

"Location and distance?"

"Mister Farrell has the course, sir. Less than two days' run."

Kirk glanced at the quiet face of his First Officer. Then he swung to the Navigator's station. "Make for Rigel Twelve, Mister Farrell." He rose from the command chair. "Let's go—there's still that jackass to skin!"

Eve's clear, fathomless eyes were on him as he entered the Briefing Room. He was too conscious of her presence for ease of mind. Masking his feelings under cool formality he took his place between Spock and McCoy. "This hearing is convened," he said.

At his nod to Spock, a bright light focussed on Walsh's face; the computer hummed. The fat man stirred uneasily.

"State your name for the record," said Spock.

"Walsh—Leo Walsh." said the man firmly.

A mechanical voice said, *"Incorrect,"* as a buzzer sounded. The man Walsh half-rose from his chair, startled.

"Your *correct* name," Spock said.

Walsh sank back. "Gentlemen, if you're going to take the word of a soulless mechanical device over that of a flesh-and-blood—"

The computer voice interrupted. *"Full data coming on screen."*

The dark girl bit her lip. She leaned toward the fat man. "If it can read our minds—"

The man brushed her aside. "No, it can't! Just what's on record, the blasted tin-plated . . ."

The viewing screen clicked and produced a sharp photograph of Walsh, lines of information appearing beneath it.

"State your correct name for the record," said Spock, again.

"Harry Mudd," grumbled the corpulent commander.

Buzz.

"Incorrect."

"Harcourt Fenton Mudd." He squirmed in his seat.

"Any past offenses, Mister Mudd?" said Spock.

"Of course not! I'm a decent, honest—"

Buzz . . . *"Incorrect. Offense record: Smuggling, sentence suspended. Transport of stolen goods. Purchase of space vessel with counterfeit currency. Sentenced to psychiatric treatment. Effectiveness disputed."*

The screen was still moving along the lines of text.

Kirk said, his voice sounding almost as cold as the computer's, "Mister Mudd, you are charged with galaxy travel without flight plan, without identification and with failing to answer a starship signal, thus effecting a menace to navigation . . ."

"A ship the size of mine in a galaxy the size of this, a menace to navigation?" Mudd said indignantly.

"You are also charged with operating a space vessel without master's papers."

"I have a master's ticket!" shouted Mudd, sweating.

"Incorrect. Master's license revoked Star Date 1116.4."

"All right! Leo Walsh, who was to be my captain for this trip, passed away sudden. I had no choice—I had to take 'er out my own self. That's why I used his name—in memoriam. Fine man, Walsh, gone to his reward."

Kirk said, "Destination and purpose of journey?"

Triumphantly, Mudd answered, "Planet Ophiucus Six. Wiving settlers."

"Say that again, Mudd? Doing *what?*" Kirk was sure he had not heard correctly.

"I recruit wives for settlers." Mudd gestured at the three girls, watching with wide eyes. "A most difficult, but satisfying . . ."

"Data on witnesses, please," said Kirk, watching Mudd. Spock touched a control.

". . . Marooned, isolated, no little woman to look after them . . ."

A light probed the three women's faces, as they flinched away. The computer hummed, buzzed erratically, and emitted a piercing squeal. The puzzled Spock, making an adjustment, removed the squeal.

Buzz-honk. *"Nonononono datadata."*

Kirk impatiently ordered the computer to go to sensor probe. Obediently, the note of the humming changed, faded and squealed again. "Any unusual readings?" Spock made further adjustments.

Eeee-hum buzz. *"No decipherable reading on females. However, unusual readings on male board members. High respiration patterns perspiration rates abnormally high, heartbeat rapid, blood pressure abnormal . . ."*

"Sufficient!" snapped Kirk.

The light turned on Mudd, the hum of the computer quieted. Mudd said smugly, "You see, gentlemen? Simply three lovely ladies. Destined for frontier planets, to give lonely men the companionship they need, the warmth of a human touch—marriage, a home, a family. I look upon my work as a public service—I've given my life to it!"

Buzz. *"Incorrect."*

Mudd made a fast revision. "Uh—I am now giving my life to the work." There was no buzz. Mudd smiled a yellow smile.

Kirk glanced at McCoy, who briefly met his eye and returned to his rapt contemplation of Ruth's dark eyes.

"Did you ladies come voluntarily?" asked Kirk.

"They did indeed!" said their self-appointed guardian. "Ruthie comes from a pelagic planet, all sea ranches. Magda there came from Halium Experimental Station . . ."

Eve's blue eyes were flashing. She stood up.
"The same story, all of us, Captain. No men.
Mine was a farm planet, with automated machines for company, two brothers to cook for and
mend for—canal mud a foot thick on their boots
each time they walked in," she said bitterly.
"I—"

"That's fine, Evie. That'll do," said Mudd.

"No, it's not fine and it won't do! We've got
husbands waiting and you're taking us the wrong
way—eyeing us like we were Saturnian harem
girls, or even—"

"That's enough, Eve!" Mudd shouted.

The girl smoothed back her golden hair with
a slim hand and, sighing, resumed her seat.

"The only charges here are against Mister
Mudd. Have you any defense to offer relating to
these charges?"

"Only heaven's own truth, which I gave you,"
said Mudd sullenly.

Kirk rose. "This hearing is closed. Mister
Mudd will be handed over to legal authorities at
our earliest opportunity."

"And us?" said Eve, slipping out of her chair.
She was suddenly close. "What happens to us?
Help me." Her eyes caught his, held them. "Help
all of us." He found his hand in hers. She was
so lovely, alone and unprotected, in the hands of
that villain Mudd—and he caught the angle of
Spock's amused eyebrow. He disengaged his hand
politely.

The lights went out.

"It's the last crystal," said Scott. "It's gone,
sir."

The darkened screen beeped and blurred. The
anxious face of Sulu appeared dimly. "Captain,
Engineering Section reports that our entire life
support system is now operating on battery
alone."

The battery system could not sustain this drain
for long. Kirks massive responsibilities flooded
back in on him. The lives of his crew were at

stake, Mudd's "cargo" was in a state of despera-
tion, the ship itself was crippled. "Mister Spock,"
he said, "Open contact immediately with the
miners on Rigel Twelve!" Mudd visibly pricked
up his waxy ears. "Advise them we'll need dilithium crystals immediately upon landing."

Alone in the briefing room with the girls,
Mudd flung his arms wide in an ecstasy of triumph. "Oh, you beautiful galaxy! Oh, you heav-
enly universe!" he cried.

The women stared blankly. He beamed at them.

"Lithium miners! Don't you understand?
Lonely, isolated *wealthy* lithium miners! They
make diamond and platinum miners look like
children digging for seashells! I'll be the richest
—" He caught sight of Eve's expression, between
enlightenment and rage. "No, no, all of us. You
girls want husbands? Not a mere ship's captain,
Evie, I'll give you a man that can buy a whole
province—a whole planet! Maggie, you'll be a
countess! Ruth, a duchess, at least!

"And Harry Mudd—?" His fat little eyes took
on a wicked gleam. "I'll be running this starship, Captain Kirk. You'll be taking your orders
from *me!*"

Ruth leaned against the doorway of Sickbay.
The crewman with the tool kit and McCoy murmured over the body function instrument panel.
They nodded, and the crewman replaced the hand
tools in his kit, closed it and rose. He turned toward the door, and stopped. Ruth met his eyes.

The doctor felt the tension. He glanced around.
Ruth said, "May I come in?"

As she smiled dazzlingly at McCoy, he stam-
mered, "By all means, yes, do!"

She dropped her head and looked at him
through her long black hair. McCoy belatedly
realized that the crewman was still goggling.
"Aren't you finished, Connors?"

The crewman offered a limp smile and a mum-
ble and slowly pulled himself out the door. The

flustered McCoy collected himself as Ruth's sea-green-clad body moved into the room.

"I was wondering what this looked like, Doctor. It's fascinating. What's this screen for?" As she passed the newly repaired panel, a light blinked. McCoy threw it a surprised glance. "I wanted to see where you work, Doctor McCoy ..." she smiled again.

McCoy was torn between the smile and the blinking light. But if she passed the panel again, she would becoming toward him ...

"Would you cross that panel again, Ruth?"

She stopped; was she dismayed? "Why? You're not giving me an examination, are you?"

McCoy shook his head. "Oh, no. I wouldn't trust my—" He broke off hastily to change the word "self" to "—judgment." But Ruth grinned with perfect comprehension. "Believe me—just come this way."

The light flashed again. McCoy frowned. "It's not supposed to do that. I've just had it fixed."

"I've been wondering," said Ruth, coming closer. "Will you be examining the miners on Rigel Twelve, doctor?"

McCoy was flipping switches on the body function panel. He was puzzled. "If they need it," he said absently.

"Well, haven't you asked?" said Ruth. "I mean, are they all in good health?"

"What? Oh. Yes, excellent. All three."

"Three?" breathed Ruth. It was like magic; three and three.

"Are you wearing some unusual perfume? Or something radio-active?"

Ruth's laugh was so full of delight that he swung round to look at her. And look again, at dark eyes brimming with pleasure.

"No," she said, "I'm just—me. Isn't it enough?"

He forgot about the blinking light.

Magda was listening raptly to Farrell, her pale hair like silver to his copper. This was a woman who knew how to listen to a man describing his work. She was just as interested in the *Enterprise* communications system as she'd been in its navigation problems. Even the speed of signals passing through space, a difficult and technical matter, seemed to intrigue her. His stride took on a new firmness as passing crewmen eyed his companion with lean and hungry looks.

Eve was on a private errand. She had located the Captain's cabin and was curled up on his bed when he opened the door.

She uncurled hastily, at his expression. "I hope you don't mind?" she said timidly.

He did mind, he thought, but not very much. "As a matter of fact, Miss McHuron, I have—"

"I was trying to take a walk, Captain. And I just had to hide somewhere. The way your men were looking at me, following me with their eyes . . ." She rose gracefully, smoothing her brief skirt, ineffectually pulling it down to cover her long golden legs.

"I'm sorry," said Kirk. "They don't ordinarily offend in this manner, Miss McHuron. But somehow, in your case, and the other ladies with you . . ."

"They're probably just lonely," she said softly, looking up at him with eyes that drew him closer. "I can understand loneliness."

Kirk broke the spell of her eyes with a wrench. "Yes, uh, would you—"

She touched his arm, and his eyes were compelled back to the bright mystery between her eyelashes. "I suppose you understand it even better, Captain, running a huge ship like this, so much responsibility every minute. And the men look up to you so." Kirk's collar was feeling tight again. He shuffled his feet.

"It probably appears more difficult than it is," he mumbled.

"I read once that a commander has to be a paragon of virtue. I've never met a paragon," she said with a laugh that sounded like music.

"Uh, neither have I," said Kirk, managing a mere gulp.

"Of course not. Nobody ever has. But some try to pretend. Do you, Captain?"

Kirk felt himself growing almost dizzy. "Miss McHuron," he began, trying for firmness. Her soft amusement engulfed him, surrounded him, lit by her eyes—her wonderful, beautiful, mysterious, compelling eyes. His dignity was cracking into tiny little pieces when suddenly she whirled away from him, and closed her eyes.

Something snapped. "No!" she said furiously. "I won't do it! I don't care what Harry Mudd says!"

Kirk blinked; his mind and senses were spinning wildly.

"I do like you!" she said fiercely, opening eyes that were pretty, and filling with tears. "I won't go through with it! *I hate this whole thing!*"

She was gone before he could find any part of his wits.

"Three of them," Mudd echoed. "You're sure that's what he said, Ruthie?"

McCoy's enchantress nodded and turned eagerly to Magda. "The miners—they're all healthy, fairly young—"

"Later," said Mudd. "Maggie, did you get to your communications man?"

"Of course," said the small woman with a toss of her pale head. "The head miner's name is Ben Childress. The others are Gossett and Bention, And they've been there almost three years—alone!"

"Three of them," murmured Mudd. "And three little brides has Harry Mudd . . ." He lumbered into a little jig step. "And dilithium crystals are worth three hundred times their weight in diamonds . . . thousands of times their weight in gold . . ."

"But they'll be down there, and we'll be up here

circling, a hundred miles away," said Ruth, cutting into his euphoria.

"And there's a guard outside your door, Harry," Magda added. "You can't even get out of your cabin."

Mudd slowed and stopped, deep in thought. Then his face cleared. "No, dear ladies. One more little job for you, and it won't be Harry Mudd that's trapped! It'll be a certain gentleman named James T. Kirk."

As he spoke the name, Eve edged into the cabin and dropped heavily into a chair. The tears still shining on her cheeks, she said, "I don't like you, Harry. And I'm not happy with myself either."

Mudd nodded. "Yes. I saw you noticing the Captain."

"We're supposed to notice them!" she flared at him. Her rebellious anger dissipated in a sigh; she leaned her head tiredly on her hand. "I don't feel very well, Harry. I think we're near the time."

Solicitous, Mudd consulted a small watch as it appeared from his pocket. "No, we've got a while yet."

"Then I need a rest," said Eve. "I'm going to my cabin."

"To dream about the Captain?" said Mudd, mockingly.

She rose and went to the door. "Perhaps."

At his station on the bridge, Farrell was dreaming of blue-and-silver miracles. Kirk's irritated voice cut through the fog of his thoughts.

"Mister Farrell, I asked for a pre-orbital course!"

Farrell woke up, sheepishly. Quickly adjusting a control he said, "Pre-orbital course locked in, sir."

Kirk swung his chair around to face all stations. "Gentlemen, that is the last order I'm going to give twice. Will you kindly make an effort to direct your attention to the operation of this ship? We are now down to battery power—and it's running low!"

A worried Scott spoke. "The battery power will get us to Rigel Twelve, Captain. But it may be unable to maintain the orbit."

"Hang us up there long enough to get six dilithium crystals, Mister Scott. That's all we need." Kirk rose to meet McCoy as he stepped out of the elevator. "Have you examined any of them yet, Bones?"

"They refuse, Jim."

"Oh, come on, you're the doctor. What's going on, McCoy?" Kirk's voice lowered. "Is it that we're tired, and they are beautiful?" He sighed. "They are incredibly beautiful."

"Are they?" the doctor answered wryly. "Are they actually any more lovely, pound for pound, measurement for measurement, than any other lovely women you've known?"

"Perhaps I lack your vast experience," said Kirk.

"Granted," McCoy acknowledged. "Or is it that these women just *act* beautiful?" He shook his head. "No, strike that. Maybe it's part of it, but there's—well, more. I'm not sure I'm making sense."

"An admission I've waited years to hear! *What are they*, Bones?"

"You mean are they alien illusions, that sort of thing?"

"I asked you first."

McCoy considered his encounter with Ruth. "They are women, Jim. Human, *female* females, I'd stake my license on that. An alien smart enough to pull this would be smart enough to prevent my medical scanner from bleeping."

"I don't follow you," said Kirk, puzzled.

"I don't follow myself."

If Mudd's women were not smart aliens, they were sufficiently smart humans. Magda's flattering attentions to Farrell had paid off. Silently, she handed Harry Mudd the navigator's communicator. "Use sub-space frequency three-nine." she said listlessly.

There were lines of weariness in her face. Mudd grabbed the instrument and flipped it open. He reached Rigel Twelve immediately. A deep male voice said, "Childress here. Come in, *Enterprise.*"

"Uh, this isn't exactly the *Enterprise.* My name is Harry Mudd. We have a business proposition to put to you . . ."

Kirk eyed the approaching Rigel Twelve on the viewscreen between anxious glances at the dropping power indicators.

"We'll make it to orbit, sir," said Farrell. "Temporarily."

"Lay in," said Kirk. "Spock?"

"We can hang up here for seventy-nine hours, Captain."

Kirk sighed with relief. "That should be plenty of time. Lieutenant Uhura, ask a representative of the miners to come aboard to discuss our needs. We'll beam him up on our first pass over their camp."

"Acknowledged, sir."

In Mudd's quarters, the three women waited. All was not well; in the lowered lights, the gleaming hair of Magda seemed leaden. Their faces were drawn and pale, and their short, close-fitting costumes were hanging limply on shrunken figures.

Eve raised her head weakly. "If you find them, Harry, you know what they are? A cheat. If you really care for someone, honestly care . . ."

Mudd's fat little hands were wedged into his pockets. They came out empty. Ruth moaned. "Care for who, Eve? Kirk? Don't be a fool. Starship captains are already married, girl—to their ships. Wait till he has to choose between it and you. You'll see."

"Why did you hide them?" whined Ruth, twisting her hands.

"I didn't hide them! I simply put them aside in case I was searched."

Ruth burst into violent sobs. She sat weeping in her chair, huddled into her loose tunic. The shrill, sharp voice of Farrell's blue-and-silver sprite cut through the sobbing like a knife. "Find them, Harry!"

He made another frantic search of his pockets. Eve watched without interest, her eyes dim. "The mattress!" he cried. "I cut a slit . . ." He lunged at the bed, and fumbled out a white packet.

With hands like savage claws Ruth and Magda seized the pills he held. Eve gazed at the colored tablet doubtfully, as Mudd offered it to her. Her tongue moistened her dry lips.

"Not a cheat, Evie," he coaxed. "A miracle. For the man who could love you instead of a ship."

She accepted the pill, and Mudd turned to look at the others. He always enjoyed watching the transformation. Magda's hair slowly turning from leaden to moonlight; Ruth's voluptuous roundness of thigh and breast returning to fill out her sea-green tunic; the lines of anxiety erasing themselves from creamy complexions.

Eve's fingers closed round the pill, as Mudd's attention was wholly absorbed. She crushed it to powder, and dropped the colored dust on the floor.

As Mudd turned to have a look at her, she rallied all the energy of her nervous system, forced it to deliver a gay vitality. Mudd saw a laughing woman, as golden as ever, and was satisfied. He beamed at her.

Kirk liked the looks of Ben Childress. The head miner was a big man, muscular, powerful —the kind of man who knows his own mind and acts on what he knows. His square-jawed face was bronzed, weathered by countless battles with the blows that man, or nature, had contrived to deal him. His stride into Kirk's quarters had the drive of a well-oiled piston.

Gossett was impressive in his own way. Younger, with a whiplash body, he stood a little to the rear of Childress.

Kirk nodded. "I'm James Kirk, Captain of the *Enterprise*. This is my Science Officer, Mister Spock." Spock rose.

Acknowledging the introduction with a nod, Childress said, "Let's get right to business. You want dilithium crystals. We've got 'em."

"Fine," said Kirk. "We're authorized to pay an equitable price."

"Not sure they're for sale." Childress paused, clearly enjoying the effect of this astonishing announcement. "We might prefer a swap."

"What do you have in mind, Mister Childress?"

The big man grinned. "Mudd's women."

Kirk eyed him frostily. Trading in women was definitely not among the duties of a Starship.

Gossett chimed in. "If we like 'em, of course. We want a good look at them first."

"Right." Childress agreed. "Trot 'em out, Captain. Oh yes—and Harry Mudd. Either way, his release is a condition of the bargain, charges to be dropped."

Kirk had liked the look of Childress, but could not say the same for the sound. "I see," he said. "Anything more, Mister Childress?"

"There's no choice for you, Kirk. You beam a landing party down, and you won't find a single crystal without our cooperation."

Appalled, Kirk said decisively, "No deal."

The two men hesitated, exchanging glances. "Captain," began Gossett.

Kirk's interruption was crisp. "You're a long way out in space, gentlemen. You may need medical help, cargo runs, starship protection. Those are facts to consider, too."

There was a silence, as the men considered. It was true that they would be virtually marooned without starship contact. As they realized the seriousness of their position, Kirk could see that he had won his point.

Before Childress had spoken, the sound of laughter came from the corridor, and a radiant Magda danced past the guard and through the half-open door. Ruth was close behind her, and the two miners' mouths dropped open. Mudd followed, unnoticed, as Eve glided past.

Ruth looked at the two, and moved in on the younger man, who swallowed, "I just bet you're Herm Gossett," she said softly.

He flushed crimson. "I—yes, ma'am. I reckon I am, ma'am."

Childress snapped out of his paralysis. He slapped Mudd on the back. "One thing I'll say for you, you're not a liar! Whee-ooh!" He stepped back and contemplated the three beauties. "And you, ladies—well, to put it mildly, you sure are welcome!"

"Childress, it's still no dea—" said Kirk. But the lights flickered and dimmed. He turned to Spock, questioningly.

"Half-power, sir. Conserving batteries."

Mudd said quickly, "I've heard they have about three days before their orbit decays and they start spiraling in."

"Thanks for the news," said Childress, heartily, with his eyes still moving from long leg to creamy shoulder.

The fat man looked at Kirk with crocodile sympathy. "I sure hate to see you suffer this kind of squeeze, Captain. But truth is truth—and the sad fact is you'll *have* to make this deal sooner or later."

Kirk was trapped, and he knew it.

Rigel Twelve was a no-man's-land of a planet. What wasn't rock was sand, a harsh grit blown by intermittent gales of cold wind that turned it to a flesh-cutting mist. Inhospitable planets were an old story to the *Enterprise,* but for sheer unrelieved bleakness, Rigel Twelve took first prize. Along with Mudd, they materialized near a low building, less than half its domed top showing above the surface dunes. Set on its metallic roof, large curiously shaped wind vanes creaked in the gusts.

Women's laughter, mixed with the lower notes of male voices, was coming from the structure. Clearly, inside there was a whale of a party.

The new arrivals crashed it. But its conviviality had reached a peak that left them unnoticed, and Kirk seized the chance to take his bearings. The room's furniture was primitive, hewn from the rock. Under the human voices the wind vanes continuously sounded, click-click-click.

Magda was sitting on the lap of the third miner, Benton. Gossett and Ruth seemed to be deeply involved with each other. Eve, alone, was staring out of a window at the vista of rock and blowing sand.

Kirk approached Childress, who was eyeing Eve cautiously. "You've won, Mister. Now, if you please, I'll have those crystals."

"When I have time, Kirk," said Childress, his eyes still on Eve. He moved toward her. She turned, and saw Kirk. Between them flashed the bittersweet acknowledgement of lost possibility, and then she moved her lips into a smile for Childress.

"Blows like that all the time," the big man told her. She could no longer see out the window—it was darkening outside. The darkness pressed against the rough glass, pitted and blurred by endless assaults from the sand.

"I . . . understand that there were originally four of you," she said.

Childress nodded. "Charley Shorr stepped out into *that* last month. You can get lost a dozen feet from your own doorway if the wind comes up sudden." As he spoke, light flashed across the black sky. It was followed by a crackling noise too thin to be thunder. "Magnetic storm. That means the wind'll really rip soon."

Ruth whispered to Gossett, "What does your place look like?"

"They're all exactly like this. I figure it ain't how a house is built—it's how it's occupied." They laughed together, intimately.

Magda, on Benson's lap, smiled her sweetest smile at him. All he could muster was a soggy grin, shaded by embarrassment. It was obvious to Kirk that he was loving every minute of it. She leaned back against Benson's shoulder. "What's that noise?" she asked idly. "That clicking sound?"

"Wind vanes on the roof," he told her. "We get all our power from those rigs, and—"

She slid off his lap and began moving her hips. Extending her arms to him, she said, "Come on, dance with me!"

"But we don't have any music."

"Yes, we do! Hear it! Click-click-click—" She moved to the rhythm of the vanes.

Dancing wasn't his forte, but she was irresistible. He went to her and, locking his arms around her slender waist, led her in very small steps to the tempo of the vanes. Watching them, Ruth reached for Gossett's arm, and smiled up into his eyes. They too joined the dance.

The wind had risen, splattering sand grit against the building. Mudd watched the dancers with genuine pleasure. Impatient and anxious, Kirk was finding it hard to contain his growing irritation. He glanced at Spock—but even his First Officer seemed to be . . . tolerant of these human games.

Then, Mudd's satisfaction waned as his eye chanced to cross the room. Kirk turned to see what had evoked the look of concern. In open contrast to the other couples, Eve and Childress had moved apart. She was . . . wilting. She looked drab and tired. Kirk could not believe his eyes. And Childress' strong face was glum.

Kirk heard him say, "Would you like to dance?"

A spasm of coughing shook her. It filled her lackluster eyes with tears. "Sorry," she gasped. "I think it's all the dust."

"That's how it is on Rigel," said Childress coldly. "All the time." He left her, and striding to the dancers, cut in on Benson. As his big arms engulfed Magda and they whirled off, Benson swore quietly. After a moment he cut Ruth away from Gossett; they were dancing dreamily close when Gossett seized Benson's shoulder.

"I'm cutting in!"

"Not on me, you're not!" said Benson, shaking him off.

Eve moved closer to Kirk, trembling and drained. She looked so woebegone, so appealing, that Kirk nearly took her in his arms for comfort. But the tension among the men had heightened dangerously; Gossett and Benson, glaring, were squaring off. Then Benson made a leap for the other man's throat.

Childress yanked them apart. "What's the matter with you?" he roared.

Eve could bear no more. She screamed. Maddened by humiliation, hurt and weakness, she burst into wild weeping. "Why don't you just hold a raffle? The loser gets me!" She flung herself toward the door, wrenched it open and was gone.

Wind and sand lashed through the open door as Kirk and Childress raced after her. Outside, the gale, smashing grit against the rocks, had broken it into fine, stinging particles.

The sky opened in a flare over Eve's head, then the blue light was gone and the darkness seemed blacker. The crackle followed her, deafening; she dropped to her knees and covered her assaulted ears with her hands. She staggered to her feet and swayed; the wind pressed her back. She had no strength to run.

Behind her, Kirk shouted, "Eve! Eve, where are you?" She wanted to answer, but her voice would only whimper. Sand pounded her face, and the wind dried her tears before she could shed them. She stumbled on, through the mist of driving sand.

Childress' search was efficient. He knew his terrain, and moved with certainty against the wind. Kirk, half-blinded, fell against a panting Mudd. "If we don't find her soon—" Another crackle drowned out the rest. Gossett's voice sounded unexpectedly. "It's gonna blow harder before it lets up!" Barely visible, he ran past.

Mudd, on his knees, begged. "Captain, do something!"

Kirk hauled him to his feet. "One chance," he said. "The ship's infrared scanner." He reached for his communicator, eying Mudd. "And when we get up there, you are going to tell me what's behind this—what's really behind it!"

But on half-power, the *Enterprise*'s scanners were sluggish.

"Checking, but not getting much, sir," said Sulu, as they reached the bridge.

"The storm is ionizing the planet's atmosphere, Captain. It's getting difficult to probe through it," added Spock.

At Kirk's elbow, Scott said urgently, "Captain, this is draining the battery even further. If we had those crystals—"

"But we don't! I didn't get them! Satisfied, Mister Scott?" snapped Kirk. Spock glanced at him, questioningly; but Spock could not know how an overload of anxiety needed expression. He shouldn't take out his temper on Scotty.

Uhura reported more bad news. "Losing communication with the miners, sir. Magnetic storm is worsening."

"Has Childress called in?"

"No, sir, he and the girl are still missing."

A downcast Scott lingered beside him. "Sorry, Scotty," said Kirk. "Just how much power do we have left?"

Mollified, Scott said, "About five hours, sir."

Mudd was wringing his hands. Kirk observed his efforts to stay out of the way, and to his surprise felt a stab of pity. Even though Mudd's crazy actions were responsible for this whole mess, he was really suffering. The frantic fat man seemed to have dwindled in his shabby uniform.

Childress had found Eve. He was carrying her limp body when he at last saw the dim light of his hut. Every muscle in his body ached from his long battle with raging winds and sand. He felt sick with fatigue as he staggered to his door, and shoved it open with his shoulder. Inside, he dumped the barely breathing girl on the crude bed, and collapsed into sleep on the floor.

She stirred. Opening her eyes, she sat up painfully, looking at the room. The floor was deep in sand, and the door was still open. More sand was blowing over the heaps of dirty clothing, tumbled piles of papers, and into the corners already knee-deep in grit. She groped her way to her feet, holding the furniture for support, and managed to reach the door. It took all her remaining strength to force it closed against the wind, and stagger back to the bed.

What passed for dawn had come when Childress awoke. He yawned, scratching his chest. Then, sitting up, he scowled as he saw his room.

Sand had been swept out. Trousers were neatly arranged on a stone chair. The bed was neatly made up, and on it lay folded shirts and sweaters. He heard metal rattling against metal. The blonde woman stood at his excuse for a stove, preparing breakfast.

He got stiffly to his feet. "I had things where I wanted them," he grumbled.

She didn't turn. "I'm eating your food. I paid for it with some chores."

He pushed her away from the stove. "And I do my own cook—*hell!*" He had touched the hot pan. He snatched his burned hand away and swore in mingled pain and irritation. She went on cooking.

"And I've not laid a hand on you," he said angrily. "Remember that!"

"Travel half across the galaxy," she said, "and male ego still sings the same old song. You want to eat or talk?" She put the plate in front of him.

"I suppose I'm to smack my lips, roll my eyes to heaven and say, 'Oh, female cooking again?'" She ignored him. He began to eat. After the first swallow, he said, "I've had better. By my own hand."

"Yes—you're tasting some of it. There are at least three layers of your leavings I couldn't scrub out of that pan."

He glared. "Find me some decent water. Then you can talk."

"If you hung your pans out in the wind, the sand would blast them clean. Or hadn't you thought of that?"

The suggestion surprised him. It also increased his annoyance.

Their breakfast was a subject of discussion aboard the lamely orbiting *Enterprise*. Childress was wolfing the last mouthful as Spock looked up from his console. "A power unit of some kind has been in operation down there, Captain. Something small—a domestic unit, heat-producing."

"That signal came from Childress' hut!" said Sulu.

Kirk left his command chair. "Have Mister Mudd sent to the Transporter Room."

"Mudd?" said Spock, inquiringly.

Kirk said from the elevator entrance, "Yes, the name of this game, Spock."

In the still-whipping sand outside his hut, Childress was stringing a line. When he had suspended a couple of pans from it, he surveyed them doubtfully. Then, shaking his head, he muttered, "It just might work."

As he opened the door, Eve was sitting at a rock-slab table laying out cards from an odd-sized deck. She didn't speak; and Childress, baffled, wandered the room for a moment before he decided to look over her shoulder.

"Solitaire?"

"Double-Jack."

"Red eight ought to go on that black nine."

"Not in double-Jack."

"You're not only plain as an old bucket," he shouted, "you're not even good company! What the devil happened to your looks, anyway?"

"I got tired of you," she said, not looking up. "I slumped."

He kicked the rock chair. Wincing, he rubbed his foot. It was her fault. Everything was her fault—everything from his sore toe to the strange new look of his home. He grabbed her angrily and hauled her out of the chair. "You hear what I said? You're *homely!* I've got enough crystals to buy me *queens!* By the gross! And you won't even speak—"

Kirk opened the door. Childress backed away. "I haven't touched her, Kirk!"

The girl looked from one to the other. She re-seated herself and resumed her game.

Mudd, pushing inside, said, "You found her out there?"

"Yes, I did. And she's been bubbling with gratitude ever since," said Childress.

"Harry. Tell him now," said Kirk sternly.

"Ah, Captain, have a heart."

"The Venus drug, Harry," prompted Kirk, tapping his foot.

Eve jumped up, scattering the cards, her hand to her mouth. Childress stared from Kirk to

Mudd. "The Venus drug," he said slowly. "I've heard of it. But I thought it was just one of those stories."

"It exists," Kirk said, with an eye on Mudd. "Illegally."

"Actually," Mudd began, "It's a relatively harmless—"

"Harmless?" cried Eve.

Under Kirk's waiting eye, Mudd pulled out the packet from somewhere in his clothing, and resignedly showed the oddly shaped tablets to Childress. "It breaks down to this," he said. "Whatever you've got, the drug gives you more of it. Men get more muscular, women rounder; men get more aggressive, women more feminine. And so on and on . . ."

"He gave this stuff to the women before you saw them," said Kirk.

The big man's fury exploded in a bellow. *"What's happened to my partners?"*

"They're married, Ben. Sub-space radio marriage."

Childress lunged at Mudd. Kirk intervened, a hand on the miner's thick shoulder. "It's fraud, Childress. They can get out of it—if they want to."

Raging, Childress turned on Eve. *"Why?"*

Mudd moved nervously in front of her. "You can't blame the women, when it was me who—"

Childress shoved him aside. "I can. A man goes out, fights, almost dies—we all almost died . . . and now that we finally get the good life in our hands, you bring us women for wives that—"

"You don't want wives!" Eve yelled. She confronted Childress, her eyes blazing. "What you want is this!" She snatched the packet from Mudd's hand. "Here's what you want, Mister Childress!" The pill went between her colorless lips and she swallowed.

It was as if Midas had touched her; the golden

glow rose in her skin, her hair began to gleam, her bosom to lift and swell. "And I hope you'll dream about this—because you can't have it! *It isn't real!*" Seductive, compelling, she lifted her clear, hypnotic eyes to the dazed Childress.

"Is this what you want in a wife, Ben? Not a woman to love you and help you—no, you don't want that! Not a mate to cook and sew and cry and need you—but this kind . . . vain, selfish, useless! Then here she is." She posed, preening herself.

Ben stared at her, speechless. Kirk said, "Quite a woman, Childress. Don't you agree?"

"A fake. Pumped up by a drug."

"No. By herself. She took no drug."

Eve dropped her pose and exclaimed. "But I swallowed it!"

"Colored gelatin," Kirk said, smiling.

Mudd nodded. "They took my drug and replaced it."

The woman, looking down at herself, was quiet. Then, she looked from one to the other of the men. Slowly she became aware that she didn't feel quite the same as she had before—under the drug. Kirk was charming, and compassionate. She gave him a smile of special . . . tenderness, not seduction. And Mudd—an absurd rogue; so clumsy in his mischief. And the big miner, proud of his appalling domestic arrangements and dreaming of buying queens. She grinned with real delight. She loved them all.

The Captain was smiling at her. "There's only one kind of desirable woman, Eve—the one who knows she's Woman."

She winked at him.

He turned to Ben Childress. "Now, sir, I've gone as far with you as I intend to. I want those dilithium crystals and I want them now," He opened his communicator. *"Enterprise, this is Kirk."*

"Spock here, Captain."

"Stand by." He faced Childress. "Do I bring down a search party?"

Confused and shaken, with his eyes on Eve—who had relaxed into neither glamorous siren nor frump, but something in between, something *comfortable*—Childress said, "No. The crystals are here, and you're welcome to them."

"We'll be beaming aboard—with the dilithium, Spock, stand by."

They all heard Scott's "Whew!" and then Spock's "How many, Captain?"

Uncertain, Eve looked at Ben. For a brief space he hesitated. Then he said, "Eve'll stay. For the day at least. We want to talk."

Mudd was peering through a scarred window. "Rather go to prison," he said, "than live in this forgotten hole." He turned his jowled, tired face to Kirk. "On second thought, maybe not. Could you see your way clear to leaving me behind, Captain? This place would be punishment enough."

"Two of us, Mister Spock." Kirk closed his communicator. "I can't leave you here, Harry, but I'll appear at your trial as a character witness—if that will help."

Mudd threw up his hands. "They'll throw away the key to my cell!"

The *Enterprise*, crystals in place at last, was heading out. McCoy, at Kirk's side, said, "Quite a talk you must have had down there. Ever consider going into the snake-oil business! That's patent medicine to *you*, Spock."

"Why work your side of the street?" said Kirk lightly. "Something wrong, Mister Spock?"

"No, Captain. I'm just glad the affair is over. A most incomprehensible and annoying emotional episode."

McCoy hit his chest. "Right smack in the old heart." He eyed Spock, and then punched himself in the lower abdomen. "Sorry. In your case, about here."

Unruffled, the Vulcan said, "The fact that my internal arrangements differ from yours, doctor, pleases me exceedingly."

Kirk grinned. It was good to be home again.

"Out of orbit, sir," said Farrell.

"Ahead full."

"Ahead full, Captain," Sulu said.

PART II

I, MUDD
by
Stephen Kandel

STAR DATE 4513.3

DOCTOR McCOY was fuming. "Am I this ship's Chief Medical Officer, or am I not?" he demanded of Spock. "This lieutenant has broken two appointments I've set for his physical exam—and no reason can I get out of him!" He stomped across the bridge. "There's something wrong with a man who never smiles, whose conversation never varies from his job routine and who refuses to talk about his background!"

"He's probably frightened of your beads and rattles," said Spock, unsmiling.

Glaring at him, McCoy tramped into the elevator. Spock looked after him. Was it amusement that he permitted to elevate his left eyebrow by a centimeter?

As to the subject of McCoy's ire, he was leaving the elevator on a lower deck. He was tall and straight, but his handsome features lost some of their appeal to an excessive regularity. He strode purposefully toward the Auxiliary Control Room at the end of the corridor. Its heavy door confronted him with "NO UNAUTHORIZED

41

ADMISSION." The Lieutenant glanced around him. He opened the door on a large room lined with computer data banks, panels, consoles.

A technician looked up, frowning. "Command personnel only, sir. You can't come in here." The Lieutenant did not even blink. He reached the technician in two steps, and placing his thumb and forefinger on the startled man's carotid artery, he squeezed. As soon as his struggles ceased, the Lieutenant lowered him to the deck, and went to work on the controls with concentrated, expert speed. A light blinked frantically; an alarm sounded. He shut them off. Then a readout panel came alive with the flash of warning lights, spelling out the words: OVERLOAD. DANGER.

The tall Lieutenant regarded them with emotionless satisfaction.

Sulu's console gave the first hint of something amiss. Alarmed, he called to Kirk. "Captain, there's an unplanned course change being fed into the instruments!"

"Correct it, Mister Sulu." For a moment, Kirk watched the helmsman vainly try to obey his order. He punched a button on the command console. "Auxiliary Control, this is the Captain. What's going on down there?"

There was no reply. Sulu cried, "Auxiliary Control is on total override, sir! I can't make the correction!"

Kirk quickly summoned Security. "Intruder Alert, deck eight, Auxiliary control." As soon as he had received their acknowledgment, he asked Sulu, "What is the imposed course?"

"Turning to 307 degrees Mark eight, sir. Being executed now."

And indeed, the main viewing screen was already showing the lateral movement of stars as the ship turned.

Kirk's intercom sounded. "Security here, Lieutenant Rowe, sir. I'm in Auxiliary Control. Ensign Jordan has been knocked unconscious—he'll be all right, though. But the directional master controls, sir—they've been mangled! They're totally unworkable."

"Any sign of the intruder?"

"No, sir. He's gone. I've put out a full security alert on all decks."

"Very well. Carry on. Kirk out." He swung round toward the Helmsman. "Mister Sulu, cut in Emergency Manual Monitor. I want that override broken."

Again Sulu wrestled with his recalcitrant console. "My instruments won't respond, sir."

Kirk called to Engineering. "Scotty, an intruder may be in your area. Rig a force field to prevent entry."

"Aye, sir."

It was too late. The anomalous Lieutenant had already slipped into the section of Engineering that housed the Emergency Manual Monitor. He silently disposed of another technician as Kirk's voice came through the intercom. "Emergency Manual Monitor, report!" He didn't turn his head. Instead, he moved soundlessly through the door to where Scott and an assistant were setting up the force field. Scott glanced up.

"Here!" he shouted. "You're not allowed to—"

He was slammed up against a wall communicator with a force that knocked the breath out of him. He hauled himself to his feet, grasping at the intercom. "The intruder is—" His words choked off.

Kirk heard the heavy sound of his fall. "Scotty! Scotty!"

The engineering assistant had seized a thick metal bar, and managed to catch the Lieutenant squarely on his handsome head. The Lieutenant didn't even blink; with the edge of his hand he tapped the assistant gently at the juncture of neck and shoulder. The man crumpled without a sound. The Lieutenant shoved him carefully aside with a foot, and moving to the main control panels, flipped every switch to "FULL

AHEAD." He then quickly removed a unit panel; as its intricate wiring was forcefully ripped out, there was a rising sound of increased power. The Lieutenant, hearing this, left Engineering at super-speed.

Sulu stared at his console. "Captain, we're picking up speed! Warp five. No, six . . . Warp *seven* now, sir!"

"Cut power, Mister Sulu!"

"I can't, sir, the controls are jammed!" Sulu was sweating with the fruitless effort to move the switches on his panel.

"Security!" said Kirk tightly, through the intercom. "The intruder is in Engineering Section. All units converge!"

"That will not be necessary, Captain." A cold, even voice cut in. The Lieutenant stepped out of the elevator.

Kirk rose. "Belay that, Mister Sulu. All right, Lieutenant—"

"Norman." Spock supplied the name.

"Mister Norman, have the kindness to tell me what this is all about."

There was no flicker of expression on the too-handsome face. "I am in total control of your ship, Captain. I have connected the matter-antimatter pods to the main navigational banks. A trigger relay is now operational. Any attempt to change course will result in the immediate destruction of your vessel."

There was something about the extraordinary Lieutenant that made his preposterous claims credible. Kirk strode to the computer station, his jaw muscles hard. "Mister Spock?"

"Confirmed, Captain. He has removed all override controls. If we tamper without knowing where that trigger relay is, we could extinguish ourselves."

Kirk wheeled on Norman. "Who are you?"

"I assure you we are no threat to humanity." There was a brief nod toward Spock. "Nor to humanoid life. We simply require your ship."

"So you 'require' my ship, do you? Who, or what, are *we?*"

Norman hesitated. Then he lifted his shirt and opened a flap in his solar plexus, revealing complex transistorized wiring.

The sight chilled Kirk. "An android!" he said slowly.

Spock was examining the mechanism with interest. "A most sophisticated one, Captain."

Norman replaced his shirt. "I control the trigger relay, Captain. I cannot be overcome by physical means, and if you attempt to use your phasers, the relay will be activated.

"We shall continue on our present course for approximately four Solar Days. At that time we shall arrive at our destination. Please believe we mean you no harm."

"I ask you again, who is this 'we' you speak of? Who sent you?"

"I am not programmed to respond in this area." "Lieutenant" Norman then froze into absolute stillness. What had seemed to be life was drained from his unwinking eyes. Kirk snapped his fingers, close to the android's face. The eyes stared ahead, motionless. He gave the figure a slight push with his hand; its heavy weight did not budge.

"Well, Mister Spock?"

"He appears to have turned himself off, Captain. And since we cannot repair the damage he's done without destroying the ship—"

"It would seem," Kirk said, "that we're going to take a little trip."

For the next four days, people warily circled the immobile presence on the bridge as they went about their errands. The blank-eyed, good-looking face stared disquietingly; the tall body in its *Enterprise* uniform seemingly inanimate.

The ship entered an uncharted quadrant; and slowed. As it dropped to sub-light speed, Norman stirred. He said, "Activate your main viewing screen, Captain."

Kirk nodded to Lieutenant Uhura. "Aye, sir."

Norman spoke again. "At this point I am programmed to inform you that we will enter orbit around our planet in seven-point-four solar minutes."

What looked like a barren ball of rock had appeared on the screen. Norman's eyes were on it. He turned briskly to Kirk. "The following individuals will transport down to our planet: Captain, Science Officer, Medical Officer, Communications Officer, Navigator."

Kirk eyed him. "Any discussions or meetings can be held here, on the *Enterprise*."

Norman eyed Kirk. "If you do not come with me, I shall destroy your engines and you will remain in orbit here—forever."

"Do you usually abduct your guests?" said Kirk bitterly.

"This is not our intention." He paused. "There is a word. Among us there is no corresponding one. But it seems to convey something to you humans."

"What word is that?"

"Please."

They materialized in what seemed to be a sort of anteroom, plain and sparsely furnished. As the party began to get its bearings, two girls approached. McCoy and Scott exchanged surprised and appreciative glances. They were beautiful, shapely, brunette, in rose draperies that revealed very human-looking bodies; among their jewels was a necklace with a number engraved on a pendant.

Norman broke the silence. "Our planet's surface is what you classify as K-type. It is adaptable for humans by use of pressure domes and life-support systems." He addressed the girl numbered "1." "I have brought them."

"He is waiting," she said.

Number 2 spoke. "If you will follow us, please." She indicated a large sliding door at the end of the anteroom. Kirk hesitated; but there seemed no alternative. He signaled his people to follow the three androids.

The door moved aside to reveal an immense chamber, carved of purple rock. Luxurious couches flanked its walls. Gilded mirrors abounded; and a bronze fountain in the shape of Venus gushed sparkling water from a golden shell. The room was somebody's dream of a potentate's drawing room . . . There was even a throne set on a carpeted dais.

At the sight of its occupant, Kirk cried, "I don't believe it!"

"Welcome aboard, Kirk. Been a long time, eh? Have a drink!" Flanked by two more of the brunettes, the lolling Majesty on the throne, wine goblet in hand, scratched his hairy chest and beamed at them.

Kirk, staggered, said, *"Harry Mudd!"*

Mudd guffawed with delight, flinging a fat leg over the arm of his throne. "To be absolutely accurate, laddie-buck, you should refer to me as Mudd the First." He lifted his goblet. "To Me, Ruler of this here sovereign planet!"

"Ruler—?" Kirk slowly recovered from his initial shock. He opened his communicator. "Harry, I want control of my ship returned immediately. We will not be your guests!" Keeping an eye on Mudd the First, he spoke into the transmitter. *"Kirk to Enterprise.* Come in, *Enterprise . . ."*

Mudd directed a casual finger at Number 2. She moved to Kirk; and daintily plucking the communicator from his hand, squeezed it into twisted pulp. "No, no, Kirk." Mudd wagged a playful forefinger. "No unauthorized communications. Tut, laddie."

Chekov asked, "Do you *know* this man, Captain?"

"I know him," said Kirk disgustedly. "Harcourt Fenton Mudd, thief—"

"Oh, come now," protested Mudd the First.

". . . swindler and con art—"

"*Entrepreneur*," Mudd corrected.

". . . liar, rogue . . ."

"Ah, did I really leave you with that impression, bucko?" Mudd shook his head sadly.

"—who belongs in jail. Which is where I thought I'd left you, Mudd."

"And thereby hangs a tale. Well, look around, Kirk. Quite a place, eh? Enjoy it?" Mudd's eyes were lurking in rolls of fat.

"Mudd, I want that trained machine of yours to de-activate his trigger relay and free my ship."

"I'll take care of that little thing, Kirk. When I'm ready."

"I'm telling you now!"

"On this planet, *I* am the one who does the telling, Kirk, old chum. *You* do the listening."

Kirk sighed. "All right. For the moment I'm listening. What are you telling?"

"You might as well get used to this place. You'll grow to love it, and that'll be nice. Very nice, because you're all going to stay here. Quite probably for the rest of your lives."

The dismay of his people behind him struck Kirk like a blow. Checkmate. This phony King had him practically squeezed off the board. He could feel fury tighten in his chest. "Harry Mudd, you are an outlaw, a liar, and in very deep trouble. *Release my ship—and do it immediately.*"

"Sorry, pal. That'd be against the law." The greasy chuckle came again. "Against my law, decreed by Mudd the First. Voted in by the resident population." He jerked a thumb at the girl beside him. "Lovely, aren't they? It's my feeling for beauty; I have decreed that I shall be surrounded by it. And all my decrees come to pass."

He leaned forward confidentially. "I've had five hundred Alices made to attend me, all identical—lovely, compliant, obedient . . ."

Spock spoke for the first time. "Five hundred, all identical? If I may say so, that strikes me as rather redundant."

"I have a fondness for this particular model. Not that I expect you, Mister Spock, to appreciate it."

It suddenly came to Kirk that conversation with Harry Mudd partook of a Wonderland quality. And his tension eased. "All right, Harry. Suppose you explain. How did you get here? We left you in custody after that affair on the Rigel mining planet."

Mudd waved a pudgy hand. "Happenstance. I organized a technical information service, bringing modern industrial methods to backward planets. I made valuable patents available to struggling young civilizations through the galaxy."

"Paying royalties to the owners of the patents?"

Mudd coughed. "Er-hm. Actually, as a defender of Free Enterprise, I found myself in conflict on a matter of principle."

"He did not pay royalties," remarked Spock.

Mudd gulped wine. Wiping his mouth on a velvet sleeve, he said "Knowledge should be free to all."

"Who caught you?" asked Kirk.

Mudd glared and started to rise. "That, sir, is an outrageous assumption!" He shrugged and sat back as he caught Spock's sardonic look. "I sold the Denebians all the rights to a Vulcan Fuel Synthesizer."

"And the Denebians informed Vulcan," added Kirk.

"How'd you know?" demanded Mudd indignantly.

"It's what I would have done."

Mudd slammed down his goblet on the arm of his throne. "Typical police mentality! No sense of humor, sonny boy. They *arrested* me!"

"Surely not!" McCoy said. "How shocking!"

"Worse," Mudd told McCoy, relishing his

apparent sympathy. "Do you know what the penalty for fraud is on Deneb Five?"

"The guilty party," Spock mused aloud, "has a choice; death by hanging, death by electrocution, death by gas, death by phaser—"

Seismic waves overtook Mudd's fat as he shuddered. "The key word, Mister Spock, is 'death.' Barbarians! I . . . left."

"Broke jail," translated Kirk.

"Borrowed transportation," glared Mudd.

"Stole a spaceship."

"The patrol reacted in a hostile manner," said Mudd.

"They shot at you."

"No respect for private property. They damaged the bloody ship. I got away, but I couldn't navigate. So I just ran into unmapped space. And here I found—Mudd's Planet."

"You would," said McCoy, shaking his head.

Kirk had lost patience. "Harry, get to it."

Spock intervened. "Mister Mudd, you went to substantial risk to bring a Federation Starship here. Logically, you must have had a compelling motivation to have hijacked our vessel."

Mudd's yellow teeth showed in a warped smile. "You'll love it here, Spock. Y'see, I found this planet with over two hundred thousand happy androids, ready to fulfill your every wish." He paused uneasily. "It's paradise."

"Then I fail to see your problem," said Spock.

Mudd pounded the arm of the throne. "*They won't let me go!*" His face flushed with anger. "They want to study me. They want to learn more about mankind!"

"They certainly chose a fine representative of it," said Kirk.

"Watch your tongue, laddie! You're talking about Mudd the First!" He leaned back, pudgy fingers drumming. "Anyway, I ran out of ideas, things for them to do. So they insisted I bring more humans here. They need more humans to study, to serve." He looked at Kirk. "I promised

them a prime sample—a Starship Captain, loyal,
bright, fearless, imaginative, and so forth and
so on. Any captain would have done." He grinned.
"I was just lucky to get you, Kirk, laddie. You
take over here, and I get off this rock and back
to civilization."

"No, Harry."

"You misunderstand me. I'm not asking you,
I'm telling you. You have no choice." He spoke to
Norman and the Alices. "Show them to their
quarters."

In unison, they answered, "Yes, my Lord."

Variously outraged, the *Enterprise* contingent
followed the androids to a side door. Near it was
what might have been another door, darkly opal-
escent. Despite his indignation, McCoy was curious.

"What's behind this, Mudd?"

Mudd chortled. "Ah. That, gentlemen, is a
shrine to the memory of my beloved Stella."

"Who?"

Mudd pressed a button; the "door" was a wall
niche. As it lit up the gaunt, beaky figure within,
clad in a long, prim black dress, began to move.

"M'wife," said Mudd simply.

"Dead?" asked Kirk, not roughly.

"Oh, no. Merely . . . deserted." Mudd sighed.
"Behind every great man, there is a woman urging him onward and upward. My wife urged me
onward and upward into space. She didn't mean
to, but she did. Her confounded, eternal nagging
—" He paused to sigh again. "I think of her con-
stantly. And every time I do, I go further into
space."

"Interesting," McCoy said. "You run away
from a woman and then bring her along, so to
speak."

"Uh, no. Not quite. I had the androids construct a facsimile of Stella, so I could gaze upon
her and rejoice in her absence." He touched another button. The android Stella burst into life.

Glaring at him, her red topknot quivering with

fury, she burst into screech. "Harcourt! Harcourt
Fenton Mudd, what have you been up to now?
Nothing you'd dare tell me, I'll be bound! We-ell,
let me tell you, you lazy, good-for-nothing skirt
chase—"

"Shut up," Mudd said happily. Instantly the
android Stella subsided into lifelessness. Mudd
chuckled. "Marvelous. I finally have the last
word!" He turned to Kirk, "With her—and with
you too, sonny boy."

Their quarters were next to a lounge that resembled a hotel lobby.

"You'll find our arrangements quite comfortable," Norman said.

Alice 1 spoke. "If there is anything you
need . . ."

"My ship," said Kirk promptly.

Alice 2 said, "We are not programmed to respond in that area."

Kirk looked away from her. "Who created you,
Norman?"

"The Makers designed us. They came from the
Andromeda galaxy."

"Then your Makers were not human?" McCoy
asked, interested.

"They were, as you say, quite humanoid. Robots were common in their civilization. We per-
formed all necessary service functions, freeing
our Makers to evolve a perfect social order."

"What happened to them?" inquired Spock.

"Our home planet's sun went nova. Only a few
exploratory outposts survived. This unit"—he
touched his chest—"was part of one such outpost
in your galaxy."

"Then some of your Makers also survived?"

"No, Captain. They died over a stretch of
time. We do not die."

"And whom do you serve now?"

"We serve Harry Mudd. He has given us purpose again. Purpose is necessary. We have lacked
it for a long time."

Spock was right, Kirk thought. This was a highly sophisticated machine. "Norman," he said, "your Makers were destroyed, and you were isolated in this galaxy. How long have you been waiting?"

"In your terms, one million, seven hundred forty-three thousand, nine hundred and twelve years, thirteen days, four hours, twenty minutes and fifty seconds."

Everyone stared at him. McCoy broke the general awe. "Well, there's one thing," he said. "We'll always know just exactly how long we've been here. Just ask . . . this unit."

And it weighed a ton, Kirk reflected. "I don't plan to be a prisoner," he said.

"You are not a prisoner, Captain. You are a guest. You are free to go anywhere you choose."

"Anywhere?"

"That is correct. Is there some place in particular you wish to—"

"Yes. My ship."

"I am not programmed to respond in that area."

Kirk flared. "I'm getting a little tired of that statement! Do you know that my ship can destroy this planet? And all you along with it?"

"An interesting reaction," observed Norman.

Spock nodded. "I, too, have always found it so. It is called anger. It is caused by frustration."

"You have fascinating mental processes, Mister Spock. I sense a kinship with you."

"There you are, Spock!" McCoy cried triumphantly. "I knew it all the time. Brother to a pile of tin."

"Beryllium, Doctor," Norman corrected. "And other alloys." If his handsome face had been capable of expressing pride, it would have done so. "We have a very well-equipped library and computer section. Our research laboratories have much to offer. You are welcome to visit there."

"All right," said Kirk. "We might, later. Now would you mind leaving us?"

"Why should we leave you?" said Alice 1.

Kirk inhaled a deep breath. "Because-we-do-not-like-you."

"A well-motivated request," said Alice 2. "We shall leave."

As they departed, Kirk turned to his officers. "Well? Opinions?"

"I think we're in a lot of trouble," Chekov said.

"That's very helpful, Ensign. Bones?"

"I agree with Chekov. We *are* in a lot of trouble."

"Spock?"

"Obviously, Captain, so many androids cannot operate independently. There must be a central control focus of some description, one which directs the android population."

"I think you're right, Spock," said the captain, after a moment. "That's where we start. Spock, you see if you can locate it. The rest of you, check around. Learn everything you can. Find out what makes this place tick. And I'll see if I can get any more out of Mudd. Let's go."

There was a central control section. Spock found it without difficulty at the end of a corridor. But all it contained was one small electronic unit. Norman was standing with his hands on it, as though in communion. Out of his *Enterprise* uniform, in the drab coverall worn by the android males, he looked even less human. He nodded to Spock.

"I trust you are enjoying yourself, Mister Spock."

"I find it almost interesting. That is an unusual device you are holding."

"Our central computer." Norman's hand rested lightly on it.

The Spockian eyebrows rose. "Oh? It seems rather inadequate for those of your sophistication. Did I understand that there are more than two hundred thousand of you?"

"Two hundred and seven thousand, eight hundred and nine," said the mathematically meticulous Norman.

"All of which are controlled through this device?"

Norman hesitated. The badge he wore began to glow. "I am not programmed to respond in that area."

"I am hardly surprised. This appears to be a simple relay center."

"It is our central control complex. Perhaps you would be interested in our computer banks. They are beyond this wall."

"Indeed? I would." As they strolled toward an entrance, Norman went on.

"They stretch for nearly ten of your miles, Mister Spock . . ."

"Fascinating," said Spock. And he meant it.

In the workshop section, Mudd and two Alices were doing the honors for Uhura and the Captain. On a model stand another android female was posed.

"This is one of our Barbara series," explained Alice 19. "The body is covered with a self-renewing plastic over a beryllium-titanium alloy skeleton."

"Most impressive," said Kirk.

"I should say so!" Uhura was enthusiastic.

"She, too, was built to my personal specifications," said Mudd. "As were the Maizies, the Trudies, and the Annabelle series."

"Don't you believe in male androids, Harry?"

Mudd shrugged. "I suppose they have their place."

Uhura, wondering, asked Alice 263, "How long would a body like that last?"

"I do not know."

"You don't know?"

"None of our android bodies has ever worn out. However, the estimated duration of that one on the stand is five hundred thousand years, before it may begin to need a few repairs."

Kirk nodded. "Economical."

Uhura was still taking in the information. "Five hundred thousand years . . ."

"Immortality," Mudd told her. "Or as near as makes no difference."

Staring at the Barbara 4, Uhura murmured wonderingly, "Five hundred thousand years . . ."

"And the best part is," said Mudd, "she'll be beautiful for every single one of those years." He appraised the *Enterprise* Communications Officer with a connoisseur's eye. "You're a beautiful woman yourself, Miss Uhura. But everyone grows old, even with the best geriatric techniques available. Yet here—you could have *that*." He indicated the form on the stand.

Alice 19 picked up the cue. "Our medi-robots are able to place a human brain within a structurally compatible android body. Occasionally, one of our Makers had it done for work on an inhospitable planet."

Mudd was saying to Uhura, "Immortality, eternal beauty; they are possible, here." He smiled his yellow smile and walked away, leaving her looking extremely thoughtful. Kirk noted her rapt expression uneasily.

Spock was saying, "I am convinced that I have discovered an important inconsistency, Cap—" when he was interrupted by the return of Mudd, followed by a beaming McCoy.

"Jim, you should see the research facilities! They've got a lab that—well, if I could spend the rest of my life—"

"Don't get carried away, Bones. Nobody's staying anywhere."

Mudd wagged his forefinger at Kirk. "Naughty, naughty. Stubborn, too."

"Well," McCoy sighed. "I wouldn't be bored, I assure you." A familiar voice was shouting outside the door. Alice 22 entered, pulling the protesting, foot-dragging Scott as though he were a recalcitrant three-year-old.

"Let me go you—you—Captain! What kind of women . . . ?"

He was released as soon as he was well inside the room. Alice 22 said serenely, "This is the last, my Lord."

"Spendid," said Mudd The First. "Long time no see, Scotty, old pal."

"Harry Mudd! So you're behind this—this—" Scott spluttered.

Kirk said, "Mister Scott, you were ordered to stay on the ship!"

"Aye, sir, and stay I did—until this female gargantua threw me into the transporter beam!"

Kirk wheeled on Mudd. "What did she mean—'he's the last?' "

"Didn't I tell you?" said Mudd blandly. "I thought I did. I beamed a few dozen androids to your ship. We've been sending your crew down to the surface for the last couple of hours. They're all down now."

Kirk seized a vase and hurled it the length of the Throne Room. His voice shook. "Are you out of what passes for your mind? You can't beam the whole crew of a starship down to a planet! Somebody has to be on board!"

"But someone is on board, Kirk. An entire crew of androids. They learn very rapidly." The yellow tecth showed in a smirk. "The fact is, Captain, I've taken over your ship completely. And there's nothing at all you can do about it."

Kirk fought back toward composure. He looked at the thief, swindler, liar. "You'll never get away with it, Harry."

"Who's to stop me?"

"Star Fleet!"

"I have a ship as fast as any in the Fleet. How will they catch me? Oh, I'll get away with it young-feller-me-lad! I'll get away with it!" He turned on his heel. "Think of it, bucko. Harry Mudd and his crew of luscious lovelies—on your *Enterprise!*"

Kirk sank down on a brocaded sofa. Spock spoke. "It is illogical to delude oneself, Captain. He could successfully accomplish this. I have questioned a number of the androids. They are totally loyal to Mudd. Perhaps what should now concern us is the fact that this android population can literally provide anything a human being could wish for—in unlimited quantity."

"I know," said Kirk sourly. "How will my crew react to a world where they can have absolutely anything they want, simply by asking? Mister Spock, bad trouble is what we're in." He stood up. "The sight of this room sickens me. Let's get some fresh air."

The sight of the Throne Room did not sicken Chekov. Wandering in, he saw the empty throne. He tried it for size. As its rich comfort embraced him, a chime rang. Two Alices promptly appeared, with carafe and goblet.

Chekov eyed them both. "You're Alice—?"

"I am Alice 118."

"I am Alice 322."

"Oh," said Chekov. "Well, it doesn't make much difference. You're both lovely."

"Thank you, Lord," said Alice 322.

At least her duplicate didn't repeat the phrase. She poured wine. "You desire something further, Lord?"

Chekov sighed. "What a shame you're not real."

"We are, Lord," they chorused.

"I mean," said Chekov carefully, "real *girls*."

"We are programmed to function as human females, Lord." It was Alice 118 who broke this astonishing news. It precipitated a large grin on Chekov's face as he looked from one to the other—equally desirable, equally well-programmed.

"That unprincipled, lecherous kulak Harry Mudd programmed you?"

"Yes, Lord."

Chekov leaned back in the throne. "This is a very pleasant place. I've seldom seen one I liked better."

In the lounge area, other members of the *Enterprise* crew were reaching the same conclusion. An engineering technician, reclining, was contemplating a bowl of grapes, between sips of wine held to his lips by Alice 73. A female Yeoman, attached to the galley staff, was ecstatically receiving an expert back rub from Oscar 114. Alice 500 was playing a lute for an entranced Ensign. A Barbara was feeding another crewman with exotic tidbits. A Trudy, transparent skirt awhirl, moved in a slow, provocative dance.

The engineering technican, summing up the general feeling, sighed, "This is heaven."

Scott had discovered the workshop. He lifted a tool. "Fantastic," he said. "Capable of handwork to the finest tolerances." He looked around him. "Microvision, nanopulse lasers . . . I've never seen anything better!"

Kirk heard the comment as he entered the workshop with Mudd. Norman was saying, "You can command us to make anything for you, Mister Scott. Or do the work yourself for pleasure. You may have the services of any number of craftsmen, exclusive use of computer facilities, anything you wish."

"Captain, take a look at this shop! It's got equipment we haven't even thought of yet," sighed Scott.

"Is this the way you're going to do it, Mudd?" said Kirk. "Hit my people at their weakest points?"

Norman answered. "We only wish to make you all happy and comfortable, Captain. If we are to serve your kind, we must understand you. Our lord, Harry Mudd, has been our only sample of your species. Now we have all of you and we are learning a great deal."

Kirk ignored him. "Mister Scott, meet me in my quarters. Tell the members of our original landing party that I want to see them."

As Mudd shrugged, Kirk strode angrily out of the shop.

In the spacious room that had been assigned to him, Kirk looked around at the familiar faces. "All right. Here we are, birds in a gilded cage!" he said. "A *cage!* So the question is, how do we get out of it?"

"I don't know, sir," sighed Chekov. "But it is a very nice gilded cage."

"We're bogged down in Mudd," said McCoy.

"I find that acutely painful, Doctor," remarked Spock.

Uhura spoke. "It *is* pleasant, Captain."

Kirk eyed her sharply. "What have you been offered, Lieutenant?"

"Sir?"

"The bribe," he told her impatiently.

"Oh. Virtual immortality, sir."

Kirk paced the length of the room. He turned back to them, his face hard. "The only way we'll be really happy is to get back to our ship. And don't you forget it! This cage may be gilded, filled with every goody any of you have ever wanted, but it's still a cage!" Anger thickened his voice. "We don't belong here! We've got a job waiting for us out there!"

He whirled on Chekov. "You, Mister Chekov, with your two pretty—servants! And you, Scotty, with the greatest machine shop in the galaxy! Uhura . . . the promise of a body that will never die. Bones and his unlimited medical facilities! Spock—what did they offer *you?*"

"I cannot, of course, be tempted, Captain." Spock cleared his throat. "However, I find their company quite refreshing. I admire the precision of their minds. And I must admit that the prospect of a flight on a ship manned by a crew that never tires, never makes mistakes . . ." He paused. "Plus an android doctor who does not consider himself a comedian, strikes me as most intriguing. There is something to be said for android society."

"All right, Spock," McCoy growled. "You stay. We'll leave. I've always found your computers better company than—"

The door opened and Alice walked into the room. Kirk barely had time to read her number before she was standing in front of him.

"Do you require something, Lord?"

The casual interruption infuriated him. "Yes, I do," he said. "My ship is what I require. I want it back."

The musical android voice replied, seeking information, "Why do you want it back?"

"Because it would please us!" Kirk shouted. "Because we desire its return to us!"

Spock added quietly, "We are unhappy here. Unhappiness is not to our best interest."

For a moment, the lovely machine-girl froze. Her pendant glowed; 471–471–471. Then she moved to Spock. "Please explain unhappiness."

"Happiness is a state which occurs in humans when all desires and wants are fulfilled."

"What wants and desires of yours are not fulfilled? It is our wish to give you happiness."

"Then give us our *Enterprise!*"

She stared at Kirk, and froze again. Once more the badge glowed. "The *Enterprise* is not a want or desire, Lord. It is a simple mechanical device."

Desperate, Kirk cried out. "She is a beautiful lady! And we love her! Can't you understand that?"

This time she froze for several minutes. The badge glowed, glared, and flared into brightness. Alice 471 buzzed and clicked. When she spoke, her voice was tinny, unmusical. "Illogical. Illogical. All units relate. All units. Norman. Coordinate." Her mechanism whirred, and stilled. Her next words came in her ordinary, melodic tones. "Unhappiness does not relate. We must study it." She walked out the door.

Kirk struggled with a repulsion mixed with pity. "Spock, you saw that?"

"Yes, Captain. The spectacle relates to an earlier conclusion of mine—to a certain cybernetic technique I observed in a conversation with Norman. I—"

"Just a minute," Kirk said. "Bones, have you made any psychological readings of the androids?"

"I have—and you can forget it. They're perfect, flawless, physically and mentally. No weaknesses, no vices, no fears, no faults. Just a sense of purpose—and there's nothing tougher to overcome, even among humans."

"We could use a little among the crew," said Kirk. "They seem to—Spock, what were you saying?"

Another Alice stepped through the door. "My Lord Mudd wishes to confer with Captain Kirk and Mister Spock."

"And we wish to talk to him. Come on, Spock."

Mudd was waiting for them near the android Stella, flanked by Alice 2 and Norman. Kirk spoke at once. "We've got a lot of questions to ask you, Harry."

"Afraid I won't have time to answer them, partner. I'm all packed. The androids will take the *Enterprise* out of orbit in twenty-four hours. It's been great having you here. Is there anything I can get for you?"

"My ship."

"You're a stubborn man, Kirk. But I don't mind that. I'll be saying good-bye to you soon enough, and you can be stubborn to your heart's content." He walked over to the alcove, and patted the robot Stella. "For the last time, Stella, old girl . . ." He pushed the activating buttons.

The Stella came to shrewish life. "Harcourt Fenton Mudd, *what have you been up to?* Shame on you! You've been *drinking* again! Ohhh, you'll come to a bad end—"

"Shut up."

The screech stilled. Grinning, Mudd placed a fat arm around Alice 2. "Alice, my little love," he said, "get my bags and have them transported up to the ship."

"No," she said.

It had been so long since Mudd had heard this word that he did not recognize it. "My bags are—" He broke off. "What's that you said, my poppet?"

"I said 'no,' " replied Alice 2.

Alice 1 spoke from the throne steps. "We can no longer take your orders, Harry Mudd."

He stared at her. "And why not?"

"Our Makers were wise," stated Norman. "They created us to serve. We have studied you and now we will serve you."

"That's what I'm telling you! Now get my bags to the ship!"

"Harry," said Kirk. "I think they have something else in mind."

"You are correct, Captain." Norman's voice was as toneless as ever. "Harry Mudd is flawed, even for a humanoid. We recognized this from the beginning. But we needed his knowledge to obtain more specimens.

"Your species is self-destructive, greedy and corruptible. You need our help."

"We find it more satisfying to help ourselves," said Kirk. "We make mistakes, we're far from perfect—but we're human. That's the word that explains us."

Inexorably, Alice 1 said, "Our Makers programmed us to serve. We will serve you by their wisdom. You will not be harmed, but we will take the spaceship while you remain here."

Panic stricken, Mudd rushed to his throne. Clambering on to the symbol of his authority, he said "No! Look here, now, you can't do that!

You—you can only serve us by obeying. Obedience, that's it. You must obey! Alice— *Yeeeow!*"

Effortlessly, Alice 1 had lifted his weight from the throne and dropped him heavily to the floor.

Groaning, he raised himself to his knees. "Kirk, tell them!" he implored.

"Norman, maybe you had better do the telling. What are your plans for us?" said Kirk.

"We shall not harm you. But we cannot permit so weak and greedy a race free run of the galaxy."

"I see," said Kirk, "And how do you intend to stop us?"

"We shall serve. Your kind will be glad to accept our service. Soon they will depend upon it. Safe from harm, their aggressive and acquisitive impulses will come under control. The galaxy will have peace—under our care."

"The whole galaxy? Controlled by androids?"

Alice 1 extended a dainty foot and kicked Mudd aside. "Yes, Captain. We have a projected figure; the galaxy will be under our control within twelve years, seven months and two days."

"And we shall serve you," said Norman, with the pride only a robot anticipating its true function can experience.

Alice 2 added, gently, "And you will all be happy; happy and controlled."

It was the contrast between what she said and the soft, feminine voice with which she said it that chilled Kirk with horror.

The hedonists had deserted the lounge area. Kirk avoided speculation as to where they were, as he looked at the pale and shaken Mudd the First. "Harry, you've given this situation some amusing aspects, but this threat from your androids is not funny."

Spock agreed. "Indeed it is not. With their remarkable mental processes, disciplined, rational, unemotional—and their unparalleled physical qualities—they quite possibly may be able to take over the galaxy."

Mudd shuddered. "Take my word for it, they can. They can do anything they make up their little mechanical minds to do."

"Whatever method we use to stop them, we must make haste," said Spock grimly. "They have only to install some simple cybernetic devices aboard the *Enterprise*, and they will be able to leave orbit."

"Spock, how do you know so much?" McCoy asked suspiciously.

"I asked them."

"Oh."

"Why shouldn't they answer questions, Bones? They don't think we can do anything to stop them."

"Neither do I," said Chekov.

Uhura gave him a chilling look. "Are you sure you *want* to stop them, Ensign? Because you seem perfectly happy here!"

"We Russians are a very adaptable people," mumbled Chekov.

Mudd had been churning with repressed rage and frustration. "You're so smart, Kirk, you and that Vulcan thinking machine of yours. Come up with something, why don't you? I'm as anxious to get off this rotten rock as you are!"

"I seem to remember," said McCoy, "you trying to leave us behind, and get away by yourself."

"Like the Russians, we Mudds are very adaptable people."

Kirk lifted a hand. "That's enough. We can't afford to squabble, we've only a few hours to stop them. Spock, what have we got to go on?"

Perhaps this time, Spock might be able to complete his sentence. "No androids, sir, no robots —even these—are capable of creative thought. As to the device they claim is their central control, it is utterly inadequate to the task of directing more than two hundred thousand of them."

Kirk nodded. "Good, So we start there. What *does* direct them?"

"There are numerous Alices, Trudies, Maizies, even a Herman and an Oscar series. But there is only one Norman."

Kirk's pulse quickened. "Noman! That's right. When I told that Alice that the *Enterprise* was a beautiful lady that we loved, what was it she said—'illogical'—"

" 'Illogical. All units relate. All units. Norman. Coordinate.' "

" 'Norman. Coordinate,' " repeated Kirk. "Why Norman—unless Norman *is* the coordinator!"

"It would seem logical, Captain. To function as they do, each android mind acts as a component of what amounts to a mass brain. The individual brain would need a link to the mass one through a central locus."

"Named Norman," mused Kirk. "The essential connection to a gigantic and highly intelligent mind. And those badges—they glow when the mass mind is called into operation!"

"The logic appears incontrovertible."

"Yes," continued the Captain. "Logical is exactly what it is. And that gives us a weapon to turn against it!"

Faces turned toward him, inquiringly. "That's it! What we need is wild, insane, irrational illogic, aimed right at Norman."

"What are you talking about, Kirk?" said Mudd plaintively. "Why are you singing and dancing?"

"About what seems to be our only opportunity," explained Mister Spock patiently.

"Opportunity?" Mudd shook his head sadly. "Spock, you may be a brilliant Science Officer, but believe me, you couldn't sell liver pills to your mother!"

Spock stared, baffled. "My mother? My mother, sir, would have no use for—"

"Forget it," Mudd said.

"Back to the point, please," said Kirk. "Harry, you said you wanted to help. Did you mean that?"

"Gentlemen, Miss Uhura, I'm with you," said Harry Mudd, sincerely. "Believe me, that wholesome, antiseptic galaxy those androids are planning—purgatory! Purgatory, gentlemen, for a man like me!"

Kirk regarded the fat man thoughtfully. "All right. The androids will be expecting us to make a break for it. That's where you come in, Harry." He nodded to McCoy, who drew a filled hypo from his medikit.

When Mudd saw it, he paled with alarm. "Now, wait a minute. I said I was ready to help, but—" Kirk grabbed one of his arms as Spock seized the other. Mudd, struggling between them, cried, "What I had in mind was advice, sage counsel, a few words of wisdom—*what are you doing?*"

The hypo hissed against his arm. He sagged, unconscious. Kirk and Spock were hard put to hold him upright.

"Harry," said Kirk, "I do believe you've put on weight."

Spock and McCoy hauled the large, limp body over to a sofa. Kirk went quickly to the Throne Room and hit a signal button. As the chime died away, Alice 1 came through the side door. There was no more "Lord-ing." She merely said, "Yes?"

"We have a medical problem," Kirk told her. "Your ex-lord Harry Mudd."

"He is human. You will have to care for him."

"We are caring for him, but our doctor needs his sickbay equipment. It's aboard the *Enterprise*," said Kirk, with urgency.

"The starship is forbidden to humans," she said.

"You've been programmed to serve!" said

Kirk, hoping he sounded sufficiently desperate.
"If you deny us access to medical facilities
on our ship, Mudd will die, cease to function!
And you—you will have failed to serve!"

Alice 1, hesitated, her badge glowing brightly.
When it went dark, she nodded. "I am directed
to observe your problem."

Mudd was sprawled on the lounge sofa. He had
recovered consciousness, but his face was flushed.
"Fever," said McCoy darkly, bending over him
solicitously.

Alice 1 obeyed orders; she observed the situation. She reached a conclusion. "He is malfunctioning."

Grimly, McCoy corrected her. "He is dying."

"If you take him to your sickbay, will he become repaired?"

"Yes." Gathered round Mudd's deathbed, they
waited for the android's answer.

"No," said Uhura flatly. The other officers
stared. She tossed her head and turned her back
on them. "They're lying. The doctor injected
something into Mudd to make him look sick. It's
a trick—a trick to get back on board the ship,
and sabotage it!"

Alice 1 made further "observations." She
noted the shock on the human faces around her,
the baleful glances directed at the treacherous
Uhura. Her badge glowed and darkened.

"The request is refused."

Kirk stepped angrily toward the beautiful
Bantu, who backed off. *"Why?"* he choked.

"I want an android body," said Uhura fiercely.
"I *want* immortality. I can be young and beautiful forever, and I want it!"

Kirk's voice was bitter. He turned to the Alice.
"All right. We tried to trick you."

"There will be no reprisals, Captain. We are
not humanly vindictive."

Uhura came closer, eagerly. "And your promise . . . You'll keep your promise? I'll get the
body?"

"Yes."

"Now—I want it now!" breathed Uhura.

Alice 1 seemed disconcerted by this human impatience. "Control Central is being prepared for transfer to the starship. It is—"

"You made a commitment!" said Uhura, stamping her foot.

"Yes. Yes." But this agreement was uncertain. The pendant again glowed and went dark. "The commitment is acknowledged and recorded." Alice 1 paused. "Programming for your body will begin immediately. The computer will complete programming before we leave."

"Thank you," said Uhura, with a triumphant look at her colleagues.

Without a backward glance, Alice 1 departed. Uhura looked a little anxiously at the others. They exchanged glances, and began to close in on her. She moved away, her hands in front of her, toward the door. Spock cut behind her, cutting off her escape. He reached the door, opened it cautiously, and peered out. He closed it, and nodded to Kirk, waiting near the cowering Uhura.

Grinning delightedly, he gripped her shoulders. "Beautiful!"

Uhura smiled. "I half believed it myself . . . Immortality. It has a nice sound . . ." She sighed.

"A human mind would go mad in a robot body," said McCoy.

Uhura shrugged. "What matters is that it worked."

"And now the escape attempt the androids expected has been made," said Spock.

"What's next?" said Chekov.

"Next?" answered the Captain. "We're going to take the Alices on a trip through Wonderland!"

Alice's adventures were to develop in the Throne Room. Kirk and Scott seated themselves on a step of the dais, while the two android girls stood guard. McCoy, idling near the door, began whistling a waltz, and his hands positioned themselves as though he held a fiddle.

The door popped open, and Uhura swept into the room in the arms of Chekov. As they whirled to the music of the violin, Scotty—getting into the spirit of the thing—began to play the bagpipes.

Alice 2 leaned over. "What are they doing, Captain?"

"Celebrating," said Kirk, smiling and beating time.

"What are they celebrating?" asked Alice 118.

"Their captivity. Are you enjoying the music?"

"Music." The Alices looked from McCoy, chin crushed against his imaginary fiddle, to Scott, mysteriously involved with his bagpipes. They turned to stare at the dancers, but they had stopped.

Chekov, stepping back, bowed deeply to Uhura. "Thank you, lovely, lady," he purred, "You dance divinely."

Uhura curtsied, dextrously managing her invisible long skirts. "Thank you, gentle sire." She rose gracefully, and slapped Chekov hard across the face.

Chekov bowed again. "You are very beautiful today!" he bellowed.

"Thank you, gentle sir!" Uhura yelled, hauling off to belt him another.

"Why does she strike him?" asked Alice 2, urgently seeking enlightenment.

"She likes him," said Kirk. He rose, calling. "Ensign Chekov! This is your captain speaking. Attention! Stand still!"

Chekov dropped into a squat, his legs flying wildly in a mad kazatsky. "Hey!"

"That's better," called Kirk.

Alice 118 spoke. "This is illogical," she said.

Kirk turned to her. "On the contrary, your staement is illogical."

The number badges glowed brilliantly; the androids immobilized. A high-pitched humming came from somewhere inside them. Chekov, in mid-"Hey!", stopped at Kirk's signal and came over, panting slightly. The androids were motionless and silent.

"It looks good," said Kirk. McCoy, taking a tricorder reading, nodded.

"Completely inner-directed. Oblivious."

"Ha!" said Kirk with satisfaction. "I wonder how Spock's doing?"

He was doing very well. His deep, deep interest in workshop tapes had impressed Alice 27 and Alice 210. "Of course," he was saying, "Your computations would inevitably lead to total description of the parabolic intersection of dimension with dimension."

"You are quite perceptive, Mister Spock," remarked Alice 27. "You possess a very logical and analytical mind."

"Yes," said Spock. Gravely, he turned to Alice 27. "I love you," he said. He then turned to Alice 210. "But I hate *you*."

"But I am identical in every way with Alice 27!"

"Of course," said Spock. "That is why I hate you. Because you are identical."

The two mechanical girls looked at each other, pendants aglow. They froze. Spock examined them with genuine interest.

"Fascinating," he said to himself, and departed for the Throne Room.

The Alices were still inert. McCoy was circling them, with tricorder open. "It certainly seems to have worked on these subordinate units. But that doesn't prove anything yet."

Spock, entering, agreed. "We have been successfully pruning the leaves and branches; now it's time to get to work on the root."

"High time," Kirk assented. "If Norman is the real control center for all of them, he should be already loaded down with what we have been doing so far. If we can double-bind the coordination center, we should immobilize all of them at one swoop. I hope. Everybody got their parts straight?"

Mudd grinned. "Kirk, old man, I'm beginning to have more respect for you. If we get out of this, would you be interested in forming a partnership? I've got a few ideas—"

"I'm sure you have, Harry. Let's go!"

Norman was standing in the control center, his fingers on the electronic unit. The attendant Alices looked up as the group came in.

"What do you want here?" said Norman.

Kirk answered. "I want you all to surrender."

"That is illogical. We are invulnerable. We are stronger."

"No," said Kirk. "We are stronger. We shall prove it. Can you harm a human you are programmed to serve?"

"No."

"But you have harmed one, Norman, my lad," said Mudd.

The badges glowed. Kirk, glancing at the others, gave an almost imperceptible nod. Mudd stepped forward, and assumed the stance of an orator.

"We humans, you poor soulless creatures, we humans do not live by bread alone. We are nourished by Liberty!" A pudgy hand waved in a dramatic salute. "For what is Man without freedom? Naught but a handful of dust—gumming up the cogwheels of Eternity?"

"Yes!" Kirk cried, passionately. "And you—all you offer us is well-being! As though food, drink and happiness meant anything to us. Don't you know we must work, we must be about our job, suffering pain and torment, labor without end, dying and crying and lamenting our burdens? Only in this way can we be happy!"

The badges crimsoned. Norman seemed confused. "This . . . is . . . contradictory . . . It is . . . not . . . logical . . . Mister Spock! Explain!"

The android turned for succor to the only remaining rational being among the captives.

Spock obliged. "Logic," he said didactically, "is a little purple bird chirping on a twig. Logic is a chaplet of pretty flowers that smells very bad . . . Are you sure that your circuits are functioning correctly?" He moved in for the final blow. "Your ears are turning green."

The androids, paralyzed, hummed. And Scott came forward.

"I am tired of happiness. I am weary of comforts and pleasures. I can't go on! Kill me! I am ready!" He threw his arms wide, baring his breast for the knife.

Obliging, the others cocked their index fingers at his waiting chest. They whistled. Scott clutched his rib cage and fell, with a last long moan. "Ooohhhhh!" He writhed. He twitched. He agonized. As he finally subsided, an Alice lurched to one side and did not straighten up.

A grinding noise came from Norman. "You. Cannot. Have. Killed. Him . . . You. Have. No. Weapons."

Kirk fell to his knees beside the prostrate Scott. "Poor Mister Scott. He had too much happiness. Now that he's gone, he will be truly happy. We shall miss him." He rose, and confronting his officers, said solemnly, "Let's hear it for our dead friend!"

Wild paroxysms of laughter filled the room. At a tiny signal from Kirk, they stopped short. Kirk struck an heroic pose.

"What is Man but that lofty spirit, that sense of daring, that devotion to duty to what cannot be sensed, cannot be deduced but only dreamed? The highest Reality! I thank you!"

"That. Is. Irrational." Norman whispered unevenly. "Il-log-i-cal. Dreamzz are. Not. Re-al-i-ty." The other Alice whirred, frozen.

Mudd snapped his fingers. "I guess it must be done. Spock, the explosive."

Reaching under his tunic, Spock withdrew a

handful of air. He molded it with care. "Please be cautious, Mister Mudd," he said. "I wouldn't want you to drop it." He pulled back an arm, wound up for the pitch and hurled the air to Mudd. Mudd leaped, reaching above his head.

"Watch out!" McCoy yelled, covering his head with his arms.

"Got it!" shouted Mudd.

Norman weaved, glassy-eyed, as he stared at them. Mudd slammed the ball of air on the computer. As McCoy moved over toward him, he extended his hand.

"Detonator," he said. McCoy handed him—nothing. Mudd carefully attached it to the air ball.

"Fuse." Again McCoy handed him nothing, a small one. It too was gingerly attached.

"Primer." But the explosive was not yet fully prepared.

"Mashie." He got one.

"Niblick." He got that, too.

"But. There is. No. Explosive." said Norman.

"No?" said Kirk. "Observe. Harry, *detonate!*"

The *Enterprise* officers cringed, anticipating the blast. Mudd pushed the plunger. "Boom!" shouted everybody at once, and fell to the floor, arms over their heads.

Norman lurched. "B-b-but. There. Was. No. Ex-. Plo-. Sion."

Mudd shrugged. "I lied."

"Harry's a liar," said Kirk. "Whatever he tells you is a lie. Understand, Norman? *Whatever he tells you is a lie.*"

Mudd grinned. "Listen carefully, Norman. *I am lying.*"

"You. Say. You. Are. Ly-ing. But. If. Everything. You. Say. You. Say. Is. A. Lie. Then. You Are. Tell-ing. The. Truth. But. You. Can'ttell thetruthbecauseeverything. You sayisalie. But. IF. You. Liethatyoulieyoutellthetruth but. You cannot. Foryou l-i-e."

Little curls of smoke were drifting from Norman's ears. "Illogical. Illogicalillogicalillogical. Explain. You . . . are . . . humans. Only . . . humans . . . can . . . ex . . . plain . . . please . . . behavior . . . ex . . . plain . . . ex . . . plain . . ."

Kirk strode up to him. With a certain glee, he said, "I am not programmed to respond in that area."

There was a harsh, grating sound. A puff of smoke issued from Norman's nostrils. He stumbled to one side, and his badge faded. He crashed heavily to the floor. Spock hurried to the door and looked out. "They're all immobilized!"

"Pity," said Scott, dusting himself off. "They could have been so useful."

"I've an idea about that, Scotty." Kirk turned to look at the grinning Mudd.

The grin wavered. "Why are you looking at me like that, Captain? Kirk, Kirk, old friend, now let's just talk this over—"

Kirk smiled, showing his teeth. "Bones, Spock, let's get out of here."

They stepped over the fallen androids, and made their way to the Throne Room.

McCoy paused at the doorway. "You must be very unhappy, Spock."

"Unhappy, Doctor? Why should I be unhappy?"

"We found a whole world of minds that work just like yours. Logical, unemotional, completely pragmatic—and we poor, irrational humans beat them in a fair fight. Now you'll be back among us illogical humans again. What a pity!"

"It pleases me greatly, doctor. Nowhere am I so desperately needed as among a shipload of your species."

"Touché for Spock, Bones!" said Kirk, laughing.

Outraged and red in the face, Mudd burst into the Throne Room. "What's this I hear about me having to stay here?" Two Alices followed him.

"Harry," said Kirk, "You are paroled to the custody of the android population of this planet."

Spock nodded. "We have already effected repairs and reprogramming on a number of the androids, Mister Mudd. They, in turn, will repair others."

Mudd glared at Spock. "But if they're fixed, we're right back where we started!"

"No. Part of the original purpose of their presence here was lost when they lost their Makers. They were to begin adapting the planet's surface for productive use. They will begin that work again."

"But what do I do? I'm no farmer."

"No, you're an—irritant, Harry." Kirk smiled. "You'll stay here to give the androids a first-class example of human failure. They'll learn to avoid other humans like you in the future."

"How long?" asked Mudd, crestfallen.

"As long as you remain an irritant. It's up to you, Harry."

Mudd straightened his shoulders, as he looked at the Alices. "Well, I suppose I can manage . . . what with one thing and another. At least I'm in touch with the galaxy again." He moved closer to an Alice. "As detention sentences go, this one isn't *uncomfortable* . . ."

Kirk turned, and started toward the door. "Oh, yes, one thing more. We've had a special android attendant programmed to take care of your personal needs," he said over his shoulder. "It may give you an incentive to work with the androids instead of exploiting them."

Mudd smirked. "Now that's unexpectedly civilized of you, Captain." The smirk suddenly vanished.

Stella, grim-jawed and uncompromising, emerged from a side door. "Harcourt Fenton Mudd, what have you been up to?" it screeched. *"Answer me!"*

"Shut up!" said Mudd frantically. She didn't. Her thin lips tightened over her buck teeth.

From another door, another Stella stalked out, black dress stiffly swaying, arms folded. "You miserable, conniving—out all night again!"

"Shut up!" shrieked Mudd, cowering. "Shut up, I order it!"

"Harcourt Fenton Mudd, you've been overeating!" screeched yet another Stella.

"And drinking!" "You need my supervision!" "You always did!" "I can see I've got my work cut out for me!" chorused Stellas, emerging from all sides.

"Kirk! You can't do this to me! It's inhuman!" Mudd started at Kirk, standing by the door with his officers. Two Stellas caught him, and lifted him by the elbows; his feet scrabbled frantically in mid-air.

"Captain!" he wailed. "You wouldn't!" Stella 500 smiled grimly. "You don't know what you're doing!"

Kirk looked back at him, and grinned.

"Good-bye, Harry. Have fun."

PART III

THE BUSINESS, AS USUAL, DURING ALTERCATIONS
by
J. A. Lawrence

STAR DATES 6273.6 — 6063.5

CHAPTER ONE

Captain's log, Star date 6273.6; Top priority message from Star Fleet Command reporting abnormal shortfall in deliveries of dilithium crystals to starbase fueling depots. All Class I Starships abort non-emergency missions and investigate. Possible Condition Red.

Accordingly, I have canceled the expedition to the Aldebaran Sector and we are heading for the planet Muldoon, the nearest dilithium source to our present position.

Chief Engineer Scott frowned over the printout message. "This could be vurra serious, Captain."

"Command seems to think it already is, Scotty. Mister Spock, prepare a chart of registered dilithium producing planets; we'll have to prepare ourselves for a systematic inquiry." Captain James Kirk of the *Enterprise* regretfully put aside the charts of the Aldebaran area.

"Immediately, Captain." The Vulcan First Officer glanced up. "It is an odd coincidence that this shortage should occur just as the new star-

ship fleet is going into service and the demand
for crystals becomes pressing."

"What do you mean, Mister Spock?"

"Just noting the coincidence, Captain."

"The Klingons!" said Sulu. "They've developed
a dilithium-eating virus!"

The Captain sighed. "Mister Spock, I must request that you control your imagination in front
of the younger officers. Some of us are a little
inclined to jump at interpretations."

"I merely remarked a coincidence, Captain,"
replied Spock coolly. "I have no imagination to
indulge."

"Of course not, Mister Spock."

"But Mister Sulu's hypothesis is not beyond
possibility, though improbable. Your charts, Captain."

Sulu, embarrassed, said, "I didn't really—"

"Never mind, Mister Sulu. Just get us into
standard orbit around the mining planet as fast
as you can."

In position orbiting Muldoon, Kirk studied the
planetary analysis. An M-type planet, just barely; low rainfall, high winds, high temperatures
... "Any personnel records, Spock?"

A cadre of twenty miners had been shippped
out four years earlier. The plant itself was, of
course, largely automatic. "They were volun-
teers?"

"Yes, Captain. And quite well paid."

"It's still a pretty bleak place to live. Anything else, Spock?"

"Apparently not, sir. Readings are within the
normal ranges for the men and equipment."

"Very well. Establish communications, Lieutenant Uhura." Thinking aloud, Kirk muttered,
"For this job we really need a commercial at-
taché, who could talk turkey and make it sound
like chicken à la king." McCoy, stopping by
with the sickbay list, grinned appreciatively.

"I beg your pardon?" said Spock.

"What about Yeoman Weinberg, Jim?" said the Doctor. "I've just had him in for his checkup, and he tells me he's aiming for the Diplomatic Service."

"That young psychohistorian? I'm afraid he might get carried away with some of those theories he keeps playing with—like the one about the Vulcan nerve pinch being a form of voodoo."

"You must admit he abandoned the theory when it became experimentally untenable," said McCoy.

"You mean when Mister Spock pinched him?" said Uhura, smiling reminiscently.

"Quite."

"Well, we'll hope he can accept less dramatic kinds of evidence when necessary. All right, Bones, I'll take him along. Lieutenant Uhura, request permission to land—for myself and the Yeoman."

Ensign Weinberg presented himself in the Transporter Room slightly breathless, and festooned with notebooks, tricorders, an elaborate Universal Translator barnacled with unexpected knobs, psychotricorder, medical tricorders ...

"What is all that stuff?" said Kirk, staring at the mass of cases, straps and lenses, under which the slight frame of Yeoman Weinberg was barely visible.

"My equipment, sir." Weinberg peered out from among the bristling assortment.

"Look, Yeoman, we aren't planning to socioanalyze these people. We just want to ask them a few questions."

"Yes, sir."

"Besides, you look funny."

"Let him take what he thinks he needs, Jim. You don't know what you may run into, even though they sounded amiable enough," said McCoy, as Kirk stepped on to the platform.

The captain shrugged. "I suppose they could be concealing something. Very well, Ensign. Let's go." McCoy shook his head as they disin-

tegrated into the shimmering transporter effect.
He would never be convinced.

They materialized outside a long hut, and the
two guests from the *Enterprise* were surrounded
by a horde of men, each trying to shake hands
and all talking at once. A large man in a maroon
pullover pounded Kirk's shoulder. "Goddamn, it's
good to see you. We don't get many new faces
out here!" Noisy welcomes urged them into the
house, out of the hot wind. They were swept into
a large cool room, ushered to comfortable chairs.
Glasses with iced drinks were thrust into their
hands. Questions, greetings, gossip flooded over
them. Yeoman Weinberg began to disentangle
himself slowly.

". . . and we have some real fresh-frozen vege-
tables we broke out as soon as we knew you were
coming. The girls grew them. Real gardening
fiends, they are . . . And you'll stay for a meal,
of course . . . We thought we'd open the Meritan
burgundy . . ." At the far end of the room, which
seemed to be a community kitchen, women were
bustling, and the sound of clattering pans floated
over the men's voices.

Kirk was trying to sort out the crowd. There
were, after all, only the twenty; Mike introduced
himself as the foreman, as he refreshed Kirk's
glass to overflowing.

"It's very kind of you, Mike, but we just want
to ask you a few questions."

"Go ahead." The foreman grinned. "As long
as it's not classified."

"I have top security clearance, if it comes to
that." A pert blonde in a checked apron offered
him a tray of little sandwiches. Yeoman Weinberg seemed to be taking a tricorder reading of
his drink—or of his sandwich.

"Then shoot," said Mike. "Al, Laro, you agree?
We tell the man what he wants to know—and
then the eats, right?"

The noise had abated; the men were listening.
They nodded.

"Right. First business, then smorgasbord!" said the pale Laro.

"Uh. We didn't know the station had been opened to families yet," said Kirk politely. "Nice you could bring your wives along. You must be a lot more comfortable." The hut was certainly well-kept.

"We didn't exactly *bring* them." A grin washed round the group.

"They joined you here recently?"

Mike nodded, and threw an appreciative look toward the kitchen. "Pretty little flock o' birds, aren't they?"

"They all seem very attractive," Kirk acknowledged pleasantly. Another plate appeared in front of him, filled with tiny colorful canapés. He waved it aside with a smile. "Mike, could you give us some production figures?"

"Sure, Captain. For what period?" He pulled a standard tricorder from his pocket.

"Current."

"Raw crystals, one million, one hundred twenty thousand, six hundred and forty-three tons over the past eighteen months," said Mike proudly.

"Where is it now?" This was the crucial question. Weinberg was holding his breath a bit too obviously, Kirk noted with some annoyance. If he was to go into the diplomatic service, he'd have to learn to hide his reactions better than this. He could start with poker lessons . . .

"Shipped out monthly, right on schedule," replied Mike, with no shadow of surprise, anxiety or doubt.

"But—" said Weinberg, and choked on a pink canapé; and had to be pounded on the back and relieved of his plate. He finally managed to enunciate, "Shipped where?"

"Captain?" said Mike, eying the flushed and earnest Weinberg.

Kirk nodded. "Those shipments have not arrived where they were expected. Can you give us the receiver's coordinates?"

Mike shook his head. "Well, damn. I wish I could, but we only load up, get a receipt for the goods, get the payment and carry on. We only mine crystals, we don't handle shipping."

Hijack. If that's it, Kirk thought, we are up against criminals who will fight. The punishments for hijacking were severe; even if we can find them, this could be a very rough assignment.

"Uh, sir," said Yeoman Weinberg. "Maybe we could ask to see a receipt? It might tell us something."

"Sure," said the foreman. "Laro, bring the receipt cassette from the office, will you?" The tall, blond man nodded and went through a nearby door.

"Mike, your crystals are not reaching the Star Base Fueling Stations. Have you any idea why?"

"Is *that* what's on your mind? Well, well . . ." Laughter rolled around Kirk and Weinberg. As Laro returned, the joke was shared with him as well. Captain and Yeoman exchanged puzzled glances.

Mike handed Kirk the cassette. "Might be because we aren't selling to Star Fleet any more, Captain."

"*What?*" Mike's easy assurance wilted slightly under Kirk's sharp question.

"Well, you see, our contract expired. We hadn't heard anything about renewing it, and we got a better bid. A lot better, as far as we're concerned. So we signed up with another outfit."

"*What* other outfit?" Kirk hoped his bewilderment was not as obvious as he thought it might be; he, too, would have to look into the poker lessons.

"Call themselves Galactic Trading Corporation, I think. That right, Al? We had such a blast with the rep—never saw a fellow with such a talent for making a party swing. Don't remember all the details . . . Here's the receipt for the last lot."

Weinberg and Kirk gazed at the display on the foreman's tricorder. The receipt was dated a few weeks back. Five thousand, three hundred and forty metric tons delivered aboard the cargo ship *Interstella*, signed by squiggle; destination unspecified; port of registration, squiggle. Utterly uninformative.

"And the contract?" said Kirk finally, looking up.

"Well now, Captain, that's not really your business, is it?" said Mike slowly. "I think we've already been more than generous showing you as much as we have of our private records. But the contract is legit for sure. Star Fleet should have renewed, but they didn't—didn't even contact us, ship didn't show up, nothing. So we're well within our rights—aren't we, men?"

There was a murmur from the others, agreeing. The friendly welcome had faded into watchfulness.

"If the contract is legitimate, Captain, and there seems no reason to doubt it, and Star Fleet dropped the option, he's right. We can't do anything about it," Weinberg said softly.

"But—" Kirk had to admit defeat. "All right. We'll report to Star Fleet Command at once" He shrugged. "I still think there was some moral obligation on your parts, Mike. After all, the plant was financed by Star Fleet."

"You could be right, Captain, you could be right. But how the hell are we supposed to read their minds?"

Somehow the invitation to eat with the miners was not repeated. Soberly, the Captain and the Yeoman beamed aboard the *Enterprise*. As they moved from the Transporter Room to the bridge, Kirk asked, "Well, Mister Weinberg, did you observe anything significant?"

"Not really, sir." The young ensign shifted some of his intruments. "Seems like it's a problem of commercial law—not my field. One funny thing, though."

"What was that?"

"Don't think I ever saw a group of women so

willing to stay in the kitchen before. Not one of them even seemed curious."

"I can't imagine what that would have to do with the problem at hand, Ensign." The bridge door opened to admit them. "Mister Spock, will you please consult your files . . . Have we anything on the Galactic Trading Corporation, or the ship *Interstella?* We'll have to find out who these people are—they seem to be moving in on Star Fleet territory—and legally!"

The First Officer busied himself with his console. "Captain," he said finally, "I am sorry. There is no information in our computer on either the company or the ship. Perhaps they are too new to have been programmed into the file when it was last up-dated."

Kirk sighed. "Lieutenant Uhura, send a subspace message to, uh, the Assistant Vice Chief of Star Base Supplies. Request information on these two matters, and report the situation found on Muldoon . . . Bureaucrats! Why don't they keep track of their contracts? Wasting our time, throwing Command into the jitters—"

Spock said thoughtfully, "Captain, it is certainly an error. But if this kind of oversight accounts for all the missing dilithium shipments, something is very seriously amiss."

"You are so right, Spock. Carelessness of a phenomenal order—"

"Or sabotage, Captain."

They looked at each other. Kirk said grimly, "We'll continue the investigation in the field until we have a reply to our message, nevertheless—if we get a reply at all. Do you remember the Coridan System, Spock?"

"Certainly, Captain. They were quite recently admitted to the Federation."

"We met your parents there," said McCoy, provocatively.*

---

*"Journey to Babel," (D. C. Fontana) *Star Trek 4*, Bantam Books.

"Yes, doctor. I take it that the abundance of dilithium in that system is what obtrudes it upon our attention at the moment, however."

"True, Spock." Kirk carefully avoided McCoy's sardonic eye. "Kindly supply the coordinates to Mister Chekov."

"I have already done so, Captain," said Spock quellingly.

CHAPTER TWO

THERE WAS NO difficulty in establishing contact with the Coridans. Uhura's board was jammed with invitations from the inhabited planets of the system. All expressed an urgent desire for the company of the *Enterprise* crew and officers, all four hundred and thirty of them if possible, with offers of entertainment ranging from clambake to corroborree.

"Me for the clambake!" said Sulu, in an undertone to Chekov.

"Not me. I'm for the poo-jah. Never heard of it."

"Well, I want to know what a clam is."

"Isn't it nice to feel so wanted?" remarked McCoy. "Whose party shall we honor with our presence, Jim?"

"Damned if I know, Bones. We can't decide on the basis of personal taste, in any case. We have business here—may I remind you all, gentlemen?"

Chekov and Sulu turned sheepishly back to their consoles. Sulu mouthed silently over his shoulder, "Clams!"

"May I suggest, Captain," Spock's voice intruded smoothly, "that we explain our mission in general terms, and then see how many of these invitations are confirmed?"

"Very logical, Spock. If they have anything to tell us—"

"—Or anything to avoid telling us . . ."

Uhura repeated Kirk's dictation on the local general band. "We are seeking an explanation of the sudden shortage of dilithium crystals. Can any of you give us any information?"

Replies came in rapidly. "Sure, after the clambake we'll have a powwow!" . . . "Honey, if you personally ask me, I'll tell you anything you want to hear." . . . "Belt up, Merman, you got the last company for dinner!" . . . "Here on Blather we keep impeccable records. Handwritten!" . . . and a muttered aside, "Blather's very strong on church suppers. Be warned."

Spock shrugged.

"Draw lots," said McCoy, helplessly.

The *Enterprise* hung in space, mercilessly bombarded by hospitality. The answer was obvious.

"We'll send a contingent to each of you. Thank you," said Kirk. He turned back to his staff. "Duty Officer, we will assign one senior officer, two juniors, two yeomen and two crewmen to each planet. As soon as all assignments are distributed, send this personnel to the Briefing Room. There's some tactful probing to be done here—clam-digging, as it were. And these clams just may close up. I want to be sure each man and woman know what questions to ask."

But Sulu, returning reeking of fish and shiny with butter, and Chekov, glistening with ghee, and all the others as the groups filtered back, reported no difficulties in obtaining answers.

"They signed a contract with the Breetish Easht Indja Company," said Chekov. "They liked the name." He grinned. His teeth were bright red. "Betel nut. You chew it. Harmless but a leetle intaxionteexi—eentocsipating."

"I thought I gave orders that nobody was to overindulge!" said the Captain, scowling.

Chekov straightened to attention—at a 190-degree angle. "Yes, sir. Deedn't kow eet was alcoholic, sir. Deedn't want to be impolite, sir. But here's a copy of their contract, sir. Very sorry, sir."

"All right, Chekov. At ease." Chekov toppled over. Sulu picked him up and set him on his feet again, where he stayed at attention—still listing to starboard.

"Good grief, it *is* the British East India Company ... Mister Sulu?"

"The Yukon Fur Trading Company, sir."

As the reports came in . . . The South Sea Bubble Company . . . The Muscovy Trading Company . . . "Vozdhrovia!" mumbled Chekov . . . The Governors and Company of the Merchants of the Levant . . . The Great Western Railway Company . . . All with the same story. And contracts.

Yeoman Weinberg was puzzled. "Those names. I've heard some of them before. The Yukon Fur Trading Company . . . and *railways?*" He snapped his fingers. "That's it! They're old Earth historical companies, part of the history of exploration and economic empires. Way back in the eighteenth century or someplace . . ."

Spock had been listening to the Yeoman with approval. "That is indeed the case, Captain. Those were the names of traders who went from Old Europe to the Eastern and newly settled territories, and established commercial relations."

"There's a bad smell in my memory around them," mused Weinberg. "I can't quite remember why."

"A great many were unscrupulous, exploitative and financially unstable. A few were of great mutual benefit," Spock went on. "Some, of course,

opened the way for political exploitation, with
effects that lasted for centuries."

"But does all this ancient history get us any
further with the dilithium problem?" said Kirk
impatiently. "All right, so there seems to be a
bunch of commercial enterprises with antique
and rather silly names. But who are they? What
are they up to?"

"Klingons!" said Chekov thickly, grinning
vermilion. "KLINGalingallingalingalons..."

Kirk turned, startled. "Mister Chekov, you're
dismissed. Go to bed."

"It could be, Jim," said McCoy, considering,
as Chekov wandered away, murmuring happily.
"They could be preparing to renew hostilities.
And if they could corner the dilithium market
..."

"We have a treaty."*

McCoy shrugged. "Who knows? We don't know
what we're up against, and that's a fact."

Kirk shook his head. "There are too many pos-
sibilities. Klingons, sabotage, hijacking—God
knows what's behind all this." He called to Lieutenant Uhura. "Please code and send an adden-
dum to our previous message to Command. Give
them all these names and get planets of registration, owners of record, all that. We'll have to
check them out. We can't interpret anything until we have those data."

Yeoman Weinberg appeared on the bridge,
looking owlish and naked without his paraphernalia. "Sir, I've been talking to the groups that
went to the parties."

"Well?"

"Sir, everybody tells me about all kinds of exotic feasts, and all kinds of hosts; but the same
comment seems to have come up everywhere
when they asked their questions."

---

*See "Day of the Dove," *Star Trek 11;* "The Trouble With Trib-
bles," *Star Trek 3,* Bantam Books.

"What comment?"

"About the agents, sir. The company representatives. They all seem to have been alike, big fellows with a lot of tall stories and jokes, very sociable. I get the impression that they sort of *charmed* the miners into signing up, even if they thought they ought to wait for Star Fleet."

"Charmed them, or conned them?" said Kirk bitterly.

"Is it different, sir, at the time?"

McCoy laughed. "Touché. It isn't, till you find out afterward."

"Funny all those reps were alike, sir."

"It would be logical to employ the same agent in the same territory," said Spock. "Except—"

". . . that these were all different companies."

"Perhaps," said Spock. "The nearest dilithium source is the cracking station on Akladi. Shall we set the course, Captain?"

The Akladian couple were almost as welcoming as the Coridans. Kirk, McCoy and Yeoman Weinberg were ushered into their sitting room, which was furnished with furs and leather. Akladi was not a planet of great natural gifts, except for the isotope of protactinium necessary for the cracking of dilithium. Clearly, there had been some luxury trading in the background.

"Well, we are surely sorry, Captain and friends. They just picked up the last prepared shipment yesterday." The short, dark man laughed. "Sorry to have to say this, but the schedule has really picked up since they bought out Star Fleet. I used to wonder if those freighters would ever get here—they were always late."

Star Fleet's record seemed to be darkening. Always late. Kirk understood that the calculations of subspace-time were extremely complex, but it seemed that everybody but Star Fleet could plunge into the continuum and come up earlier.

"This is my wife, Andree." A cuddly redhead

had emerged from a doorway. She grinned and held out her hand.

"Hi, Captain, Doctor, Mister Wombat."

"Weinberg, please, ma'am, thank you. How do you do?" Weinberg was frankly goggling. She was delicious.

She looked at him under long eyelashes. "I do fine, do you?" She chuckled.

"Sorry, Captain and all. I'm afraid Andree's been celebrating. She only got here yesterday and she likes it."

Kirk smiled faintly. The man's fatuousness was understandable, but he wanted to ask—"

"Bought out Star Fleet?" said Weinberg, scratching his head with the corner of a tricorder.

"Andree, please. Not now." She was switching knobs on a music console, and the beat of dance music roared out at them.

"Oh, come on. We have company, Joe! Our first visitors—we should have singing and dancing, not boring talk about buying and selling!"

"I wanted a girl with some life in her," said Joe, with apologetic pride. "I guess I got me one." Andree was whirling on one shapely leg, her rosy skirts flying. "Oh, look out, baby!"

She had slipped on the polished stone floor, and fallen against the corner of the console. The music squawked; Joe and McCoy reached her a second ahead of Weinberg and Kirk.

"I'm fine," she said, already on her feet, and holding Joe's hand. "Didn't hurt a bit."

McCoy's medical tricorder was in his hand. "I'll just have a quick look at your shoulder—you're likely to have a nasty bruise at least . . ." He frowned, and adjusted the instrument. "That's funny. Captain, I think my tricorder is malfunctioning. I'm not getting a credible reading."

Joe stepped between his wife and the doctor, who looked up with surprise. "It seems to be all right now. What the—"

"What's the matter, Bones?" said Kirk sharply.

"I am getting normal, healthy, human readings from Joe here, and no protoplasmic reading whatsoever from the lady."

"Is that possible, Doctor?"

"Only if she isn't human."

Joe's face was scarlet. "You don't have to go on and on about it, buddy."

Kirk tried to smooth him down. "We meant no offence, Joe. Can you explain?"

"Look, why don't you and your gang go back to your ship instead of interrupting our honeymoon? Andree thought a party would be fun, but you guys—"

"I'm sorry, Joe, but some explanation is due us as representatives of Star Fleet. First, the shipment expected from you has not reached Star Base 152. Second, you claim that someone has 'bought out' Star Fleet, which doesn't make sense. Thirdly, and this may be a merely personal matter and it may not, your very charming wife arrived on the same day that the prepared crystals left, which needs clarification—whatever she is."

"Look, fellow, we don't owe you any explanations. But I will tell you that this station is the property of the Vocational Training Institute, and the fat joker who collected the shipment was their accredited representative." Joe was speaking with dangerous distinctness. "And you are trespassing on Institute property and will you kindly get the hell out of here!" He ended in a shout.

"*I'm* the payment," said Andree, sweetly. "On a kilo per kiloton basis. Worth it, don't you think?" She danced around the little group. "And now, having worn out your welcome, will you please do as Joe says and go away someplace."

They beamed aboard the *Enterprise* in thoughtful silence.

"Add the 'Vocational Training Institute' to the list, Uhura."

"You got that about the 'fat joker,' sir?" said Weinberg.

"I did, Yeoman, I did. What do you make of this, McCoy, Spock?"

"I wish I'd been able to take readings on those women you saw at Coridan," said McCoy. "I can't help wondering if maybe they, too, were—not human."

"If they aren't human, what are they?" asked Weinberg blankly.

"Androids. Robots. Artificial people."

"No wonder they didn't mind staying in the kitchen," muttered Weinberg.

". . . on a kilo per kiloton basis . . . Spock, can you calculate the weights of those twenty 'wives' on Muldoon, and see if it matches up with their production?"

"Captain, unless you know the actual weights of these androids, I can only guess at the ratio that would apply if they were average human females. And there is no reason to assume that they are . . . However, on the basis of a 56-kilo average weight, it would check out. Highly unreliable," said Spock, radiating disapproval.

After considerable further delay, Lieutenant Uhura reported a reply to Kirk's earlier message —from the Assistant Vice Commissioner of Inventory Accounts, to whom the message had eventually been referred.

"The companies listed are registered to the following—do you want me to read out the whole list, sir?" asked Uhura doubtfully. "There are about fifty names here."

"No, just give me a printout. Anything else, or just fifty names?"

"Yes, sir. Their addresses . . . But they're all the same!" She stared at her readout display. "All fifty are based on the planet Liticia!"

"That is distinctly odd."

"We may be nearing an explanation for some

of the common factors, Captain," said Spock.

"The fat joker, for one."

"Yes, Doctor. And the—flavor of those company names."

"There's more coming in, Captain," called Uhura. "Six other starships have reported similar findings, with companies buying up lapsed contracts—and all leading to Liticia. And they want a report on dilithium supplies on board the *Enterprise*."

"Obtain that information from Mister Scott, Lieutenant, and pass it on. Where is Liticia, Spock?"

"We have no information on a planet of that name, Captain," said Spock, after a few moments.

"Well, of all the dunderheaded—wouldn't you think they'd have the sense to send us coordinates for a new-registry planet!" said Kirk crossly. "Lieutenant, compose a polite request. If I try, I'll say something rude."

Uhura smiled. "Of course, Captain."

"Jim, the question of sabotage is still open."

"I suppose so, Bones. What do you think, Mister Spock?"

"If what we think we suspect we know may be considered evidence, Captain," began the Vulcan, with distaste, "it would follow that hijacking has been eliminated; possible sabotage could be responsible for the non-renewal of contracts by Star Fleet; and the Klingons are still a possibility. I feel, however, that this summary is totally syllogistic and its logic so theoretical as to be a deception. On its own bizarre terms, it is unlikely to be both sabotage and Klingons—unless the Klingons have infiltrated headquarters, a probability of two in five billion, seven hundred million, fifty-three thousand, two hundred and one, in view of the Organian monitor."

"And the fat joker?"

"That is puzzling," admitted Spock. "Unless he is the hypothetical Klingon agent."

Kirk laughed. "I thought you didn't have any imagination, Spock."

"I do not, Captain," said Spock repressively. "But I do have an extrapolative faculty. A *logical* extrapolative faculty."

"Captain Kirk! The coordinates for Liticia have just come in! They are just a little late in transmission."

"That's headquarters for you. Just a little late —again. Set our course, Mister Chekov. Those coordinates are in our sector."

"Star Fleet Command is now pointing that out, sir," said Uhura.

A little later, Chekov spoke out of a reverie. "Captain?"

"Mister Chekov?"

"We've been here before, sir. I knew those coordinates were familiar! It's—Mudd's Planet, sir!"

Kirk choked. McCoy winced. Spock raised his right eyebrow.

CHAPTER THREE

To THE BRIDGE'S collective amazement, permission to land was immediately forthcoming. Kirk summoned Doctor McCoy, Mr. Spock and Yeoman Weinberg to assemble in the Transporter Room.

Mr. Chekov also presented himself.

"Yes, Mister Chekov?" inquired Kirk.

"Nothing, sir. I—remember Mudd's Planet, I wondered if—"

"No, Mister Chekov." The Navigator's memories were all too pleasant; that was evident from his expression.

"Yes, sir." Wistfully, Chekov watched the four men shattered into sparkling nothingness as the voice of the doctor faded . . . ". . . and I never will approve of it. I was attached to my atoms, had them for years . . ."

"Well, well, well! If it isn't a veritable reunion! Hello, Captain James T. Kirk. I have found it in my heart to forgive you." Fatter than ever and bulging out of a rather grubby pink tunic, Harry Mudd opened his arms in welcome. "How very delightful of you to drop in. No, do not speak." He held up a meaty hand. "Do not tremble, friends. I hold no grudges. Indeed, our encounters ever leave me with a challenging new situation. You always relieve my ennui."

He gestured toward a lane of tall trees. "Refreshments, gentlemen. This way." Long tresses of scented flowers wound through the branches. The road was paved with marble and curved toward a pale, glimmering building in the middle distance.

"My house," said Mudd modestly. "I rather took to the design. Saw it in a book somewhere."

"It's the Taj Mahal, Captain!" whispered Weinberg. "An ancient tomb, I think."

Crystalline waters of a pool reflected the towers, cool and still. "A *bijou* residence, isn't it, laddie?" Mudd flung a solid arm across Kirk's shoulder.

At the door, a tall figure salaamed, its plumed turban brushing the paving. The door swung silently open; and a phalanx of decorative black-haired beauties, all alike and clad in diaphanous trousers, beckoned them in.

"Uh—as you know, I have a taste for the more agreeable things in life," said Mudd, with a sidelong glance at the *Enterprise* party. " 'Mid pleasures and palaces though you may roam, be it ever so humble, there's no place like home.' Well, it's best to combine them, in my view."

"Home," said McCoy sententiously, "is where the heart is."

"Exactly so, my boy, exactly so. Whose heart could fail to be won by such a home?"

The rooms within were varied. A marble hall of perfect proportions led into a cosy salon, and then into a drawing room draped with velvet.

Yeoman Weinberg was silent. More and more harem beauties emerged, until the very walls seemed to undulate.

McCoy whispered, "They're all androids, Ensign. Don't let it get to you. He's a very persuasive character, this Mudd."

There seemed to be acres of feminine bounty before the dazzled eyes of Yeoman Weinberg.

"Fully programmed, of course," added McCoy.

"Of course," Weinberg gulped. A voluptuous dark-eyed temptress glided past, and smiled.

"Yeoman! You are on duty!" said McCoy sternly.

"Yes, sir. On duty, sir." The Yeoman hastily fumbled with his tricorders. This seemed to steady him slightly. He looked up. "Sir? Mister Mudd is the only one here besides ourselves who's *real?*"

"That's it."

"Wow, sir," breathed Weinberg.

". . . and this is my sanctum sanctorum." Mudd waved them through a pierced stonework arch. Carpeting curled round their feet as springy as new grass. Set in the center of the floor was an illuminated aquarium, covered by thick glass. As they crossed it, multicolored fishes darted among waving grasses under their feet. Chairs rolled up behind them, inviting.

"You've outdone yourself this time, Mudd," said Kirk.

"Do you think so? I am delighted to have your opinion to confirm my own. Aruhu, bring refreshments." Mudd waved languidly from his chair at a veiled figure, which bowed and withdrew.

"I rather like the Aruhu's costuming. One wearies of display occasionally. Don't you agree, gentlemen, that the hidden beauty is the most enticing?"

"Where are the Stellas, Harry?"

"Oh." Mudd moved comfortably. "Transmogrified, laddie. I turned her into a spaceship. I thank you for the opportunity to forget her once again. I do so enjoy forgetting her." He heaved a great sigh of contentment.

"Harry," said Kirk, "pull yourself together. We

want some nice, clear explanations. What are you
up to?"

"That's *her* favorite line," complained Mudd.
"I'm not up to anything. Nothing at all. Just living the life of the idle rich."

"Let's start there. How did you get rich?"

Indignant, Mudd heaved his bulk upright. "I
am a salesman, am I not? I am an excellent salesman, if I do say it myself."

"He means con man," muttered McCoy.

"You malign me, doctor. A con man is dishon-
est, a low criminal type. I am very, very legitimate. Even the new name of this planet is
'Legal.' I learned my lesson."

"All right, so you're a salesman. What are you
selling and who are you working for?" persisted
Kirk.

"For myself, dear boy, for myself. Ah, here's
Aruhu with refreshments."

Led by the veiled one, jeweled nymphs poured
into the room, bearing golden trays heaped with
fruits—pomegranates and pineapples, smooth and
prickly pears, wines and cakes and sweetmeats.
Perfumes seemed to rise from the carpet as they
glided across it. The lights from the aquarium
shone softly variegated colors through the air,
rhythmically echoed by tinkling music.

"It's like a dream," murmured the bemused
Weinberg.

"It'll get more like one in a minute—Jim! He's
got the air full of soporifics!"

"Mmmm? Oh, has he? Who?" said Kirk, yawning.

"Captain, wake up! Mudd, you go too far!"
With effort, McCoy jumped to his feet. Spock
shook the captain by the shoulder, as the Yeoman
slid to the floor in a clatter of instruments, snor-
ing.

"Doctor, don't you have an antidote?" snapped
Spock.

"Mm. Right here," answered McCoy, toppling
over.

Spock, apparently unaffected as yet, bent over
the prone doctor and pried the hypospray from
his lax fingers. Within a few moments the *Enterprise* contingent had recovered its senses and
the perfume had wafted away.

"Now what was that all about?" said Kirk
with irritation, as he got up from his so-soothing
chair.

"Just wanted to make sure you would relax, as
my guests," said Mudd sheepishly. "No harm intended. Guess I misjudged the dosage."

"Let's get some fresh air," said Kirk, disgusted.
"You had orders to develop this planet with the
androids. Let's begin where we left off. What
have you done about the planet, besides giving
an accommodation address to God knows who?"

"I'm so glad you asked, Captain." Mudd's smile
threatened to split his ample cheeks. "By all
means, fresh air." He snapped his fingers. "The
five-seater to Door Seven, immediately."

They filed down a tapestried corridor, which
opened on to a vast courtyard. McCoy said to
Weinberg, "You can't let your guard down for
one minute with this man."

"I can see that," answered Weinberg thoughtfully. "It looks like he is really behind the crystal
shortage, somehow."

"It appears probable," agreed Spock.

A small sleek aircar was waiting in the courtyard. "Gentlemen, we will tour Liticia in style.
You can't possibly see a whole planet from the
ground, after all." Mudd bowed them toward the
moving glideway that led to the open door of
the car.

"And he is always plausible," added McCoy.
"Remember that." Weinberg nodded.

Captain Kirk hesitated. The entire landing
party should not be entrusted to the pudgy and
treacherous hands of Harry Mudd. But he wanted
the experience and judgment of both Spock and
McCoy with him; and that left only the unsea-

soned Weinberg, who had shown signs of suc-
cumbing to the succulent attractions of the Mudd
Mahal. Obscurely, Kirk felt that it would be essential to guard their flank. Well, Ensign Weinberg was On Duty.

"Yeoman, you remain here. I want you to keep
your communicator open both to us and the *Enterprise*, so that nothing is happening that is unknown to us all."

"Yes, sir." Weinberg stepped off the glideway
and began searching among his equipment for his
communicator. He moved away from the aircar.

The Captain, Spock and McCoy seated themselves on soft-cushioned chairs. The car floated
upwards, its engines humming softly, and Mudd
said, "A drink, gentlemen?" Trays, already filled,
unfolded across their laps. "This little car
flies herself. She's programmed for a grand tour,
and a grand tour you shall have."

"Last time we were here," observed McCoy,
"you had to live under a dome—this planet was
uninhabitable on the surface."

"So glad you noticed that, dear boy," said
Mudd. "Yes, we have created an Earth-type atmosphere here—a little ecology-juggling here, a
little chemical balancing there, and eureka!
Nothing to it, when you know how. We have
techniques for accelerating natural processes—
and of course, where we can't, a little mechanical
know-how—for instance, the trees in that wood
behave like trees, look like trees, produce oxygen
like trees, but they are trees like the girls are
girls. Fully programmed."

"Wish you would pass on some of those techniques to the colonists," said Kirk, thinking of
some of the bleak and barren places where settlers
were struggling with nearly unlivable planets.

"Certainly," said Mudd, surprised. "If they can
pay . . . Hmm. Could be quite profitable. Tell you
what, laddie, you could do some splendid adver-
tising for us—on commission, of course."

McCoy rolled his eyes to heaven. Spock snorted. Kirk withered Mudd's brashness with a freezing stare.

"Uh. We have now passed the perimeters of the central complex, and you will see, radiating outward from it, arable land under intense cultivation. Three to six crops a year, all for export, of course."

"Real crops?" said McCoy. "Or fully programmed potatoes?"

It was Mudd's turn to originate a withering stare. "Doctor, I don't think you can be paying attention. A fully programmed potato would be absurd.

"There to the west, please observe the former Patchwork Desert, now known as the Patchwork Farm Area. Underground, we have discovered deposits of wulframite, petroleum and various rare earths. Over the area to your right, you will observe the refining and chemical plants. Just beyond these hills we will see Landing Field Six."

"Talk about fully programmed," muttered McCoy, yawning.

Small cargo vessels were landing and taking off from the field. Single rails for freight transport radiated from the field to convenient depots for the industries. Mudd's Planet had been developed to the last millimeter.

"All right, Harry, you've made your point," conceded Kirk. "Now tell us what happened to the Stellas we left to guard you?"

Mudd sighed. "I grew very, very weary of her voice. I never was anything but weary of her voice. Either they shut her up, or I went mad, that's what I told them. So they—cooled her off."

"Out of pity?" said McCoy ironically.

"Compassion, laddie, compassion. *You* wanted me to suffer; *they* could not bear to watch my torment."

"You talked them out of it," said Spock.

"But you said you turned her—them—into a spaceship?"

"Recycled, dear boy, recycled. All my ships are Stella now. *Interstella, Stella Sapphire, Dark Stella, Evening Stella* . . ." Mudd smirked.

"And now the real question, Mudd," said Kirk quietly, as the aircar circled Landing Field Fifty-seven. "Kindly explain the connection between you, this . . . weird consortium, that's been traced to this planet, and the dilithium crystal shortage. And I want a straight answer, Harry!"

"I'm a businessman, laddie. A salesman. I sell," began Mudd.

Losing patience altogether, Kirk shouted. *"What do you sell?"*

"Androids, of course."

"Female androids," said McCoy.

"Of course."

"Incorrigible!"

"Well, why not? There's still that great hungry market out there, all those outposts of mankind, poor lonely men grinding and working, year after year without companionship, slowly drowning in their own dirt. Oh, I make myself weep sometimes, just thinking about it." Mudd drew a none-too-clean sleeve over his eyes. "Android women are very adaptable. And they present no difficulties with their appearance, either."

"You just can't stop selling women, can you?" said Kirk with loathing.

"You wound me, Captain, you really wound me. Androids are not *people!"* said Mudd, aggrieved. "Surely you, of all people should know that I have been taught a lesson. One cannot trade in human beings. That would be immoral. But these robots didn't belong to anybody, their Makers had vanished. They *need* to belong to somebody. It makes them feel secure."

Spock stared. "Mudd, sometimes I can follow your rather baroque trains of thought. But machines do not feel a need for security. Try that again."

"But they do, Spock laddie. You don't understand them as I do," replied Mudd earnestly.

Spock shook his head, as if to clear it. "Either these androids are machines, in which case they do not have feelings—and, Captain, they can be classed as salable property; or, they are sentient beings and cannot be anyone's property. Kindly repair your argument."

"Try thinking of them as rather clever animals, Spock," offered Mudd kindly. "That may help you out. And they're still salable."

Weinberg's voice burst tinnily from the communicator. "There was a time when that line was applied to anyone unlucky enough to have been captured and enslaved. The feelings of animals didn't matter—even long after the slave and his grandchildren were free!"

McCoy said soberly, "That's sadly true. We have progressed enough to allow the rights of sentient beings to all intelligent life-forms. In those days, slaves were allowed to have souls occasionally, but treated as non-beings. Do androids have souls, Spock?"

"That is not my department, Doctor. I have never encountered a satisfactory definition. But these androids are delightfully clear thinkers."

"Why is this discussion getting so theological?" said Mudd plaintively. "The fact is that there was a whole planetful of ownerless machines here, and plenty of capacity to produce more. And there's no law against selling machinery. My ownership is indisputable—all my business enterprises are registered legally."

"What prices do you get for androids, Mudd?"

"Sufficient, laddie, sufficient. Have you a warrant to audit my books?"

"They must be very expensive. Kilotons of dilithium crystals, for instance," Kirk persevered.

"Of course my girls—uh, machines—are expensive. Look at the design. Look at the workmanship. And you wouldn't believe the overhead . . ."

"And in what coin do your customers pay?"

"Ah, that's another story." Mudd took on a

mournful air. "Poor, lonely lads, they don't always have many credits. But"—he brightened—"they have the fruits of their labors to sell, sometimes. Yes, Captain, I've picked up many a strange load on many a far planet. I could tell you stories—"

"Dilithium crystals," said Kirk firmly.

"Why do you keep harping on dilithium crystals? What are they, some kind of jewel? Have I missed something?"

The car climbed, and banked over a low range of hills.

"Your memory is failing, Harry. You know very well what they are. And Star Fleet is not pleased about this shortage. Not pleased at all."

Harry Mudd shrugged. "My heart is wrung, laddie, really wrung. But there's not a thing I can do for Star Fleet. Have you seen enough of Liticia? Shall we go home and freshen our drinks?"

"If you can manage to refrain from doping us. But here or on the ground, we're going to get some answers out of you . . . Come in, Yeoman Weinberg. Have you been listening?"

"Yes, sir. A very interesting discussion, sir. Lieutenant Uhura agrees."

"Lieutenant Uhura?"

Two voices replied. "Yes, sir?"

"You've got an echo. Clear your line."

"Is this better, sir?"

"No, Lieutenant, it is not."

"She's right here, sir. I don't think she can reach her equipment from here," said Weinberg.

"Lieutenant? I didn't give you permission to beam down."

"I didn't, sir. I'm right here at my station," came a slightly indignant answer.

"But she's right here next to me at the—the Mahal, sir," said Weinberg, sounding bewildered.

"Mudd, what's going on?" said Kirk in dangerous tones.

"A little surprise for you," said the fat man

hastily. "I was saving it for later. Just a moment." The aircar drifted to a stop in the courtyard. The glideway slid from the door, and Kirk, seizing Mudd by the collar of his pink jerkin, pushed him out of the car.

"Ooof. You've been putting on weight again. Now, what's all this about Uhura? Where is she?"

Yeoman Weinberg ran up to meet them. On his heels followed the veiled houri; there was a familiar laugh. A slim hand reached up and touched veiling, and as it dropped, Uhura's superb tawny face smiled out from the draperies.

"A replica, Captain. You may recall, we had your Uhura's specifications. Our Aruhu is really a charming personality—so like your officer, but perhaps a little more . . . accessible," Mudd purred.

"Lieutenant Uhura, aboard the *Enterprise*," Kirk called.

"Sir, what's going on, please?" Uhura sounded, reasonably, concerned.

"They've made an android copy of you."

"Of me? Why?"

"Mudd likes you."

"Huh. Can she sing?"

"Of course I can." The "Aruhu" began a low, oddly cadenced melody. Uhura, on the *Enterprise*, joined in after a surprised moment.

"At last I have done something that pleases you," said Mudd, expanding visibly. "They do sound pretty in duet, don't they? How about a choir? Shall I summon the other sixty-seven?"

Uhura broke off and squeaked. *"Sixty-seven?* Of *me?* . . . Oh, that's too much, sir. I don't like it, Captain. It's—it's almost insulting!"

There was an uncomfortable silence. Weinberg broke it.

"You mean they can duplicate *anybody?*"

"They can, obviously," said Kirk.

"Then why can't he be a replica, too?" said Weinberg, indicating Mudd.

Kirk blinked. Spock and McCoy exchanged glances. "There's one way to find out!" McCoy grabbed his medical tricorder and flipped it open.

And Harry Mudd ran, much too fast for a fat man, through the open gate at the end of the courtyard. Kirk and Spock sped off after him at top speed, but when they reached the gate, he was out of sight. "Spock, you go toward those trees; McCoy, we'll go that way . . ." As Kirk was starting off in pursuit, a voice behind them spoke.

"Ah, what a pity. I'm afraid that unit had a faulty panic button. But it did very well with dialogue, didn't it?"

Mudd stood there in the yard, smiling ruefully.

Kirk became aware of fury. There seemed to be no end to this runaround, and no answers. "All right, Mudd Number-whatever-you-are, no more playing games. Give us some information. Where are the dilithium crystals and what's happened to the real Harry Mudd?"

"What are these dilithium crystals, Captain?"

Kirk moved threateningly toward the chubby android who so resembled Mudd. "Don't give me that! They are the crystals Mudd—or you—have been collecting from the miners in exchange for the females. Now *where are they?*"

"Captain, I remind you that it is useless to threaten us physically. Let us be reasonable. We have recently been learning much about law. Harry Mudd talks of little else. Writs, sir. Subpoenas, sir. Habeas Corpus and mandamus. Have you these in hand? For if not, we need answer no questions. So we have been told."

"Spock!" said Kirk desperately. *"Do* we have writs and mandamuses?"

"Captain, I believe that our commission from Star Fleet constitutes a legal mandamus over this planet, as it is within United Federation territory."

"Is this a belief or a fact, Mister Spock?" said the android anxiously. "If it is a matter of faith, it carries no recognizance, but if incontestible fact, our position is *de jure* rather than *de facto.*"

"What's he saying, Mister Spock?" asked the bewildered Weinberg.

"It looks like Mudd, it sounds like Mudd, but by the Ratiocination of Irm, it thinks like a Vulcan!" said Spock, with unwonted vigor. "If we have Federation authority to ask the questions, the answers are also authorized by the Federation. If necessary, we can produce a form of mandamus in *locum tenens.*"

"Mister Spock, are you *enjoying* this?" said McCoy incredulously.

"You cannot appreciate the pleasures of rationality, Doctor. These beings are *logical,*" said Spock.

Kirk said patiently, *"Now* can we ask about the crystals?"

Having observed that there had never been any prohibition nor constraint against the Captain's *asking,* and that, presumably, in his undisciplined way, the Captain was inquiring about *answers,* the android replied. "The Human Mudd is not comprehensible to us. His actions are only logical by his own logical constructs, based on his own peculiar premises. He was quite insistent about a course of action to which he referred as 'covering his tracks.' We do not see the necessity for this, following upon behavior in strict accordance with the law, but—"

"Where did he go? Where are the crystals?" Kirk was beginning to feel that he would never in all his life be able to say anything else. Nor would anyone ever answer him.

"You are impatient, sir. I was trying to proceed in an orderly fashion from one concept to the next. However, since you wish to omit the intervening steps. I will tell you that the Human Mudd has left this planet with his entire stock of dilithium crystals."

"Where did he go? How?"

"The Human Mudd gave us instructions to construct a ship rather more efficient than yours, and controllable by a small crew of androids and himself. It is essentially a highly maneuverable cargo ship, capable of great speeds. He insisted on giving it a name, instead of a nice, clean number," said the mechanical Mudd distastefully.

"Where did he go?"

"I cannot tell you that."

"Just a minute, Captain," said Spock to the fuming Kirk. "You cannot tell us, due to lack of knowledge or to inhibition of programming?"

"Lack of knowledge, Mister Spock. May I say that it is remarkably easy to communicate with you?" said the android.

"Thank you," said Spock gravely. "It is not surprising, Captain, that Mudd avoided telling the, uh, local population where he was headed. He was able to program them to protect him up to a point, but even Mudd must have known that he was not sufficiently able to understand their logic to be able to secure their silence. No doubt he expected us to penetrate his smoke screens—he will have gained time, however."

"Suppose the androids have to get in touch with him about the business?" asked Weinberg. "Can they reach him?"

"It will not be necessary," said the android simply. "We are capable of managing this planet and its affairs without assistance from the Human Mudd."

"Aren't you even curious?" said McCoy.

"I believe that is an animal attribute, Doctor, not a mechanical one."

"Define the need to deduce from evidence," said McCoy, challengingly. "Define, 'I believe.'"

The android started to speak, and stopped. It turned to Spock. "I—you—I sense a paralysis in my logic circuits."

"The need to deduce is wanting to know. That is curiosity," said Spock. The android quivered. "As to 'I believe'—a conversational phrase only in that context, doctor, without meaning."

"Spock, I am not sure you are human at all, if faith is meaningless to you," said McCoy.

"Either curiosity is an animal attribute or it is not," mused the android doubtfully. "If it is—" Abandoning philosophy for the moment, he said, "If this planet is subject to your legal authority, we must therefore assist you. Therefore we will override the orders that the Human Mudd left with us. In what way can we be of use?"

The android led them back inside the Mudd Mahal. The girls had vanished. Weinberg was disappointed—and relieved—to note. Kirk explained, as they crossed a high-ceilinged hall, that the *Enterprise* and the other ships of the Fleet had already checked the planets likely to be ports-of-call for the Litician cargo ships, and there had been no sign of Mudd, or large quanities of crystals, in the vicinity. "His trail ends here," said Kirk.

"He must have a hide-out somewhere," said McCoy.

"Somewhere in the galaxy," said Weinberg. His words pointed out the hopelessness of their task.

"Can we have a look at wherever he worked—if he did work?" asked the doctor. "Maybe we can find a clue there."

"He had a habit of closeting himself in here, occasionally," said the android, opening a door. It led back into the "Sanctum."

"What a place to try and concentrate!" said Spock with disgust, eying the sensuous movement of the fish and the play of lights.

"He had access to the Central Computers from here." The android Mudd sank into the chair that had been occupied by the other replica, and lifted the covering from its right arm. A small console was embedded under the cushion. "He could, of course, control the sounds, lights and air composition from this, as well."

"He couldn't have made a flight plan out of his head," said Weinberg.

"No. He must have used the central computer.

Can we check its records?" asked Spock of the android.

"Certainly, but it seems improbable that he would have confided his plans to the computer, if he was eager to remain hidden."

"Spock, can't you inspire this lot of tinware to come up with something useful?" muttered McCoy.

"Inspire, Doctor? You flatter me. But it is true that Mudd could not have planned his course without the computer. Can you check out all information retrieval records stored in its memory banks?" he asked of the android.

The android nodded. "It will take some time. We will be glad to help you, since we dislike being under-informed. Perhaps you, and this medical gentleman who seems to think in the same framework as the Human Mudd, would direct us."

"You are a rotten replica of Mudd," said McCoy.

"All ships of the same model are not identical, Doctor. Come, let us expand the limits of our knowledge."

"I still think they have no souls," muttered McCoy to Weinberg, who nodded politely.

CHAPTER FOUR

IT TOOK SEVERAL days to work through the information stored in the computer on Liticia. In the end, even Spock looked a little haggard. Mudd had indeed covered his tracks; all that could be found was a series of short gaps in the memory banks, where something had been asked, answered—and irrecoverably erased.

Aboard the *Enterprise* hovering over the planet, officers and the android Mudd sat in dispirited conference.

"Let's go through it again," said Kirk tiredly. "We may have missed something. I would like to thank you, Mudd II, and all the androids who can communicate through you, for all your help.

"Harry Mudd has escaped with the entire current supply of dilithium crystals, in a new and superior ship. He has a crew of androids, who are now out of touch with their home planet. We have no clue whatsoever as to where he was headed, nor what his intentions may be."

"Female crew, naturally," remarked McCoy.

"As you say, Doctor. The new vessel, the *Su-*

perstella, is capable of speeds exceeding our own and, of course, has unlimited supplies of crystals. And it looks to me as if we will have to report failure to Star Fleet. Mister Spock?"

"I'm sorry, Captain. You have stated the problem accurately."

"Mudd—androids?"

"We can add nothing further."

"Anybody? What do we do now?"

Into the ensuing silence, Uhura called tensely. "Captain!"

The message from Star Fleet was unprecedented. The Klingon-Romulan League had approached the Federation, requesting a temporary alliance to deal with the dilithium crystal shortage. Ships of Star Fleet, and the great war armadas of Klingon and Romulan alike, were paralysed.

And only the *Enterprise* had reported sufficient supplies of crystals on board to remain in operation for any reasonable time. "Therefore, by the authority of the Joint Council *pro tem* of the United Federation of Planets, the Klingon Empire and the Romulan Empire, the *Enterprise* is ordered to use any legitimate means at her disposal to procure the crystals from the present proprietor. Immediately. This is an emergency. Repeat. This is an emergency."

Mr. Scott turned pale. "This means—"

"The whole galaxy at a standstill. And only we have any chance of breaking it," said Kirk heavily.

"Who would have thought one fat joker could cause such havoc?" said McCoy.

"Engines silent, everywhere," mourned Scott. "Och, aye, nothing *worrrking . . .*"

"Harcourt Fenton Mudd, a random element in an orderly universe," said Spock. "He has no connection with anything but himself, and is therefore totally unpredictable."

"And a criminal," added McCoy.

"Is he?" asked the android. "He has been so

careful to stay within the limits of the law. We know of none he has broken."

"So we couldn't even arrest him," said Kirk bitterly. "Even if we could find him, we have no recourse but to *pay* him for his tricks. And how are we to locate an unknown vessel without coordinates, sensor readings, not even a sector?"

Uhura said, "We could try the collar-button game."

"The what?"

"You know—if I were a collar button, where would I be?"

"What's a collar button?" said Weinberg. McCoy whispered something to him. He nodded thoughtfully.

As Spock and Mudd II turned and froze Uhura with identical stares, McCoy said aloud, "I remember that. But it's not really very helpful, Lieutenant."

"Sir?" said Weinberg. "It isn't logical, it's all a matter of imagination, if I understand what the Doctor just explained. What else can we try? If we tried to pretend we were in Mudd's shoes, follow his train of thought, it might lead us somewhere . . ." He trailed off.

Doubtful, Kirk said tentatively, "The only one among us who could be familiar with his trains of thought would be Mudd II. Could you—"

The android who so resembled Harry glared. "I must remind this young human that I am *not* Harry Mudd, and that we regard such irrational proceedings as wholly meaningless."

Spock rose from his chair and sat down near the android. He did not speak, but it was clear that he aligned himself with the forces of reason.

"But the rational approach hasn't got us anywhere," said Weinberg. "All that work with calculations and computers, and we're stymied. Isn't there anyone here with *something* in common with the real Harry Mudd, who could try?"

"Yeoman Weinberg, I find your remarks entirely out of order. Harry Mudd is an aging delinquent, a criminal—"

"Not proven," said the android.

"—and a liar, and no member of this ship's company answers in any way to that description."

"Of course not, sir. But he has other characteristics as well—he's devoted to pretty women, he loves luxury, he's clever and spirited and optimistic. Doesn't anyone share these with Mudd?"

Several pairs of eyes glanced at the navigator's console.

"What are you all looking at me for?" said Chekov, startled.

"Mister Chekov," said Kirk, smiling, "If you were Harry Mudd, where would you be?"

"Please, Captain, I hardly know the man. I can't imagine."

"Mister Chekov," said Weinberg, leaning forward earnestly, "think of Mudd's Planet, as you first saw it. There were all those *temptations*, remember?"

Chekov's tongue ran round dry lips. "I remember."

"You *were* tempted, Mister Chekov," said the captain.

"Yes, sir. But so was everybody else, sir."

Kirk sighed, acknowledging the truth of this. "Yes, Even Mudd liked it, until the androids wouldn't let him leave. You don't like coercion either, Mister Chekov?" he added hopefully.

"No, Captain. But who does?"

"I don't think Mister Chekov feels any sympathy with Mudd whatsoever," said Spock. "I am not at all sure that it is proper to press him."

"That's not quite true," said Chekov. "About some things—girls, for instance." He hesitated. "I wouldn't ever go Mudd's way, not ever, but sometimes I have daydreamed a little about the life on that planet—the one we couldn't have . . . I . . ." said Chekov, uncomfortably. "I'd never have said so, but you seemed to think I could help in some way, and so . . ."

"Mister Chekov, I think I speak for us all. You have remarkable courage," said McCoy reassuringly. "None of us were so above temptation as all that. I remember that laboratory . . ."

"But Bones, the laboratory did not interest Harry Mudd, except as a means to an end," said Kirk. "And yes, Mister Chekov, I do indeed agree with the doctor. Are you now volunteering to try to imagine you are Harry Mudd, and what you would do in his position?"

"All right, sir. Yes, sir."

"Well, try."

Chekov shut his eyes and frowned in concentration.

"You have a ship full of supplies everybody in the Galaxy wants . . . They're all after you, *Harry* . . . If you can just find a place to hide. Think of it, *Harry*, where will you go to be safe?" said Weinberg helpfully.

"May I point out," remarked Spock, "that this repellent effort could include the fact that Mudd is now in a position to control the galaxy?"

"Power, *Harry* . . . the power to ask anything— luxury, women, all the wealth of the galaxy— if you can only find a place to hide . . ."

Chekov's brow was knotted. "I am having leetle trouble imagining all that. It's not possible, not conceivable. Not for me. I wouldn't want so much power—I couldn't handle it."

Kirk was not displeased; Chekov could not even imagine being irresponsible.

"Oh, he's too inhibited!" said Weinberg with impatience. "Doctor, can't you give him something to loosen him up a little? Hypnosis, a drug— anything?"

"I could not," said McCoy. "It would be most unethical."

"Please?" said Chekov. "Eef I can do anything to help, and we cannot afford not to try—I am willing."

"I don't like it," said McCoy. "It can be dangerous messing about with the inhibitions of a trained officer. They can be vital to his or his ship's survival."

"But sir, the question is now the survival of all the ships in the Galaxy. Isn't there something you could do—a tranquillizer, a light trance, nothing drastic or dangerous . . ." urged Weinberg. "As long as Mister Chekov is willing, it wouldn't need much."

Chekov looked at McCoy and nodded. "I am not afraid of anything you would do, Doctor McCoy. You would never do me harm, nor harm the *Enterprise*."

"Doctor." Kirk's voice was utterly neutral—neither a request nor a command—something uncertainly between the two.

"All right," said McCoy reluctantly. "But if it doesn't work with a very light trance, we'll have to find some other line of investigation."

"Like what?" said Kirk, meeting his eye. "Do you think I would agree to anything so farfetched as this if we could think of something else?"

McCoy, resigned, pressed a hypospray to Chekov's arm, and sat down facing him.

"Relax, Pavel. Everything is all right now. Just relax, and let your body feel easy . . ."

"Yes, Doctor." Chekov's eyes dropped shut. His breathing grew slow and regular.

"Your name is Mudd," said Doctor McCoy. Someone suppressed a giggle. Spock winced. "Harcourt Fenton Mudd . . . You long for riches, and soft women. You can never get enough . . ."

"Mmmmmm," murmured Chekov, smiling.

McCoy went on, under the fascinated eyes of the bridge. He described Mudd's face "in a mirror"; his ambitions, his quest for riches and power. ". . . And now you are on board your powerful new ship, the *Superstella*, laden with your loot . . ."

"Horse," said Chekov, firmly. "No ships."

"On the *Superstella*, filled with rich cargo . . ."

"Khabardar!" shouted Chekov, slicing his right arm through the air. Puzzled, the group exchanged glances.

"Where are you headed, *Harry?*" continued the doctor gently.

"To Kuban we fly, in the steps of Iskander and the Khan . . ."

"Kuban? Check that, Spock," whispered Kirk.

Spock, shaking his head, bent to his console.

". . . Tana and Sarai will never rise again. Timur has conquered! . . . I am sore, bring rugs . . ." Chekov's voice fell to a whisper and he lolled in his chair.

"Wake him, Bones," said Kirk sharply.

One leg stretched out before him as though stiff, Chekov was rolling back and forth, and muttering.

"Pavel Andrevich, you are relaxing into sleep. Sweet, dreamless sleep . . . All is well. You will waken slowly, very slowly, and when I call your name you will awaken . . . *Pavel!*"

Chekov sat up and rubbed his eyes. "What happened? Did we find him? Did it work?"

McCoy sighed with relief. That trance had been rather deeper than he had intended.

"We don't know yet. Spock?"

"There is a planet called Kuban in Sector 27-F, and another called Sarai in Sector 29-G. No registered planet called Tana. Neither of the two planets have any dilithium crystal trade or production."

"That didn't sound much like Harry Mudd," said Scotty doubtfully. "What was that about a horse?"

"We should have asked him more questions," said Kirk, drumming his fingers on the arm of his chair.

Chekov looked disappointed.

"I disagree, Jim," said the doctor, uneasily, "He didn't sound like Mudd to me either. But hypnosis is a delicate business—he was either going further under, or coming out. He gave you two planets—what more do you want?"

"I suppose we could hardly expect more. But it's so vague . . . However, Mister Chekov, we do thank you."

"What did I say?" asked Chekov. The recording, played back to him, merely baffled him. "I don't get it," he said. "What was that foreign word? It wasn't Russian—I don't even know it. And I've never seen a horse. It didn't mean anything."

"Not to your conscious mind," said McCoy.

"And I don't think that was anything like Mudd," said Chekov finally. "Are we going to— what was it—Kuban, Captain?"

"Have we any choice?" said Kirk wearily. "It's about as reliable a clue as a feather in the wind, but it's all we have."

The android Mudd II, expressing himself as thoroughly shorted out in his logic circuits, took his leave. Spock watched his departure wistfully.

"You don't approve of this, Spock."

"Captain, I am virtually beyond comment. My logic circuits are also shorted out."

"I'll confess something, Spock. So are mine. But at least we have a direction in which to start, rather than sitting here going around in mental circles."

"I will acknowledge that, Captain. For whatever it may be worth. You could as well have stuck a pin in a star map, however."

CHAPTER FIVE

THE PLANET KUBAN was rocky, barren and uninhabited. There was no sign of a living being upon it.

Across in Sector Twenty-nine-G, the planet Sarai was a hive of activity—a transit station for goods entering and leaving the sector.

"It might be just the place to hide—the purloined letter principle," said Weinberg. "Who'd notice one more ship among this crowd?"

"I don't think you understand the principles of planetary traffic control, Yeoman," said Spock drily. "Every parking orbit is assigned and known. We could inquire if the vessel has been here; they will know."

But the *Superstella* had not been admitted to orbit at Sarai, and was most definitely not among the ships presently loading or offloading.

"That's that," said Kirk. "It was a pretty fragile clue." He sat in his command chair, looking at the floor.

"I let you down. I didn't find him," said Chekov, sadly.

"Not your fault, Mister Chekov. Your subconscious is not Harry Mudd, for which we must all be very thankful."

Sarai courteously requested that the *Enterprise*, if their business was concluded, kindly make way for incoming traffic. And no, their facilities had never been used for transshipping dilithium crystals. The great starship headed for intersteller space.

They lingered, hopelessly, aware of time running out. When Uhura reported an incoming message, Kirk cringed inwardly. It would be Star Fleet, transmitting its urgent orders once again. And he had nothing to report.

"That's funny." Uhura nudged her controls. "It's—Captain! It's *Mudd!*"

Everyone crowded to Uhura's console. "He's broadcasting on a general band—a blanket message. It must be reaching clear across the Galaxy! He says—he wants bids for two hundred kilotons of crystals, Captain!"

"What's he done with the rest? Where is he?"

"He's building up his price, Captain. He can afford to feed the supply back into the system slowly and expensively. And when it's exhausted —he still has those contracts," said Spock.

"Uhura, can you locate him? The coordinates?"

"That's very difficult, Captain."

"Trace the radio direction, Lieutenant."

"Sub-space radio doesn't work like real-time radio, sir. Once the message is coded into subspace transmission, it becomes a part of the Dirac beep. Unless the message itself contains coordinates, you can't possibly trace a single message to its source."

"The Dirac beep?" said Weinberg.

"Sub-space contains all messages ever sent, or to be sent, simultaneously. Our receivers tune in only to messages especially coded, Yeoman."[*]

"I see—I guess."

---

[*]For details, see "The Quincunx of Time," James Blish.

"But you can tell if he is near this sector?"

"Yes sir. By the wave-decoding factor. He is in this quadrant."

"Hell and damnation!" said Kirk.

"Captain, he'll have to give directions for receiving his bids. Just wait a little longer," said Spock.

"You're right, Mister Spock. Here it comes," said Uhura. "Minus 72 Mark zero range 59 kpc, sir."

"An area of 38,792.473 cubic parsecs, Captain. Rather a lot to search. He seems to be in the globular cluster NGC 104 in the constellation Tucana—close to the Romulan borders. It's not going to be easy to find one ship in a cluster, Captain," Spock said from his station.

"Aye, Captain. The electromagnetic radiations alone are likely to foul our instruments," added Scott.

"Are the stars so close together as to make it impossible to negotiate a course, Spock?"

"No, Captain. This cluster is Concentration III —the closest are about half a light-year apart. The odds are much in our favor. But a search pattern is going to be exceedingly complex."

"Considering the odds against us an hour ago, Spock, it seems to me that they are much improved. Set the course for Tucana, Mister Chekov!"

The viewscreens, adjusted for real-scale image, showed a startling sky. The light from the Galaxy was drowned in the glow of the thousand suns of the cluster. Too dense to be seen as constellations, the stars of its core merged into a blue-white brilliance, casting the shadow of the main hull sharply over the propulsion nacelles. Suddenly the shipboard lights seemed weak and dim. The officers and crew of the *Enterprise* gazed at the dazzling sky.

"Any sign of Mudd, Spock?" said Kirk at last.

"The sensor interference is very heavy, Captain. If he's hiding in there"—Spock indicated the blazing heart of the cluster—"it may not be possible to locate him. He's chosen the best possible refuge."

"Hmph," said Kirk. "Lieutenant Uhura, send a message to Harry Mudd. 'Space Fleet regards your actions as highly irregular and a violation of commercial ethics. No bid will be forthcoming. The *Enterprise* is closing in on you. You are advised to surrender and return in the custody of the *Enterprise*."

The viewscreens wavered, and the visual displays at Uhura's console burst into whirling colors. "The Space-noise Blanking Control can't cope with all this interference, Captain. There's a message coming in, but I can't get it clear."

". . . clkgl . . . brmmm . . . first quality lot . . . thirty thousand cred . . . Klingon representative . . . Code eight-three-two—do I hear—." The voice faded, and returned.

"To . . . *Enterprise*, greeting . . . to hear from you again . . . dropped out of my little auction . . . forty, Regulan Group Four . . . pity, isn't it . . . Federation . . . immobilized . . . forty-five? Going at forty-fi—"

"He's really holding an auction!" said Kirk, amazed. "How can anybody be bidding? Klingons, Romulans—he must be mad."

"I don't think so, Jim," said McCoy. "He's bluffing. We know that the Klingons and Romulans can't be bidding, but he doesn't."

"Do we, Doctor?" said Spock darkly. "I am still unsatisfied that all is well at Headquarters."

"Captain!" said Sulu. "There's a cold body among that group at 35 degrees 7 minutes—look!" The viewscreen focussed in on a cluster within the cluster, eight spectacular double stars. "I've screened out the background light. Somewhere in there is either a small dead star—or a ship!"

Kirk gritted his teeth, and growled, "After him!"

The *Enterprise* surged forward, passing so close to the stars that one could reach out and pluck them like grapes, Kirk thought. So close and so bright . . .

"There he is!" The scanners showed the unmistakable pattern of a ship.

The communications panel exploded into loud life. "Will you be good enough to get out of my sky, sir?" Mudd's face appeared, apoplectic with rage, on the screen. "This is not Federation Territory and you have no business here trespassing. You intrude!"

"I am authorized to deal with you, Harry, wherever you are. Are you coming quietly?" Kirk hoped his voice did not reflect the uncertainties that he felt—the matter of the bidding, the doubt about Star Fleet's saboteur—

"Dear me, James Kirk. Will you never learn? Why do you hound me across the universe, ruining my business enterprises, destroying my honest efforts at rehabilitation—you have no grounds to arrest or detain me, and well you know it!" boomed the crackling image. "I have broken no law—and anyway, we're outside the range of the law. Go away, Kirk, go away. Or I shall have to take steps."

"Don't threaten me, you—oversized hooligan!"

"You'd be better advised to place a bid, Kirk, than to waste your breath abusing me," said Mudd unperturbed. "For you, a discount, because we are old friends. Only forty thousand—a once in a lifetime offer!"

"Why, you—what makes you think you can steal property and sell it back at double prices to the rightful owners? You have damned funny ideas about the law, Mudd."

"I am the rightful owner, Captain. I bought and paid for these crystals. And haven't you heard of inflation, laddie? What with the cost of labor nowadays, all over the Galaxy the same story. What can a poor businessman do in times like these? Am I supposed to take a loss? Am I in business for my health?"

"Is he in range of the tractor beam, Scotty?" hissed Kirk on the intercom.

"I canno' be certain, Captain. But one wee jump, and we've got him."

"One more chance, Mudd, before we haul you in. Do you come voluntarily?"

"Not on your fuzzy yellow jerkin!" said Mudd, and vanished.

"Lock on!" shouted Kirk.

"We can't, sir. He's gone. Dodged us."

Kirk flung himself to Sulu's console. "Where he goes, we go. Follow him!"

They dived into the center of the cluster, Sulu's brow was beaded with sweat; all his helmsman's skill was called into play, instantly reacting to the information that was reaching him in furious cascades of numbers. Suns whipped invisibly past, red and blue and white, the ship shuddering as the computers compensated for gravitational attractions and the vast amount of radiation.

"We're losing him, sir."

"Warp Factor Seven."

"He's too far ahead, and gaining," said Chekov. "He's headed away from the plane of the Galaxy, Captain! He's accelerating toward the Barrier!"

"Mister Scott—warp factor eight!" Tight-lipped and grim, Kirk snapped the order.

"Captain," said Spock urgently. "Are you sure this is wise? We can't take the risk of meeting the Barrier."

"I'm going to get that rotten jailbird of the Galaxy if it's the last thing I do!" Kirk's eyes were slits of determination.

"Captain, you may be taking the *Enterprise* on a disaster course," said Spock very quietly.

The ship plunged on in the wake of Harry Mudd and the dilithium crystals, the protesting voice of Scott rising in pitch along with the sound of the engines.

Kirk relaxed slightly. "All right, Spock. I admit he gets my goat—but we have orders to recover those crystals. What do you suggest we do, crawl back to Command and tell them we were scared to chase him? It's not just the *Enterprise* at stake, it's the whole Galaxy!"

"If we become lost in the Barrier, sir, it won't save the Galaxy."

"We're gaining, Captain! We're gaining on him!" said Sulu.

Kirk looked straight at his First Officer. "Get him!"

The shuddering of the ship had lessened. They were streaking through the clear, dustless space between the last sparse stars of the Galaxy—and the Barrier of incomprehensible energies that encloses it. Mudd's ship was plainly detectable. The whirling arms of the Galaxy lay far above them . . .

Sulu waited for orders, his hands poised for immediate action. His console showed the pinpoint light of the *Enterprise* rushing toward the blazing red warning diagram of the Barrier sphere—where starships are unnavigable, and the mind of man breaks down with overloaded senses.* The tiny light of the *Superstella* reached the red zone, and winked out.

"Warp *Nine*, sir? The ship canno' take much more!" said Scotty from the Engine Room. "Are you sure, Captain?" The ship's motion was no longer smooth; a high whine was drilling into their skulls.

Voices clamored at Kirk, anxious, worried; Scott, Spock, McCoy, all doubting him, wanting to turn back, to abandon the precious cargo carried by that pirate Mudd—

---

*"By Any Other Name," *Star Trek 6;* "Is there No Truth, No Beauty," *Star Trek 10;* "Where No Man Has Gone Before," *Star Trek 8*, Bantam Books.

The light on Sulu's screen reached the corona of the Barrier . . .

"Khabadar!" Chekov leaped from his chair, charged across the bridge, his arms rising and falling. McCoy seized him.

"What's the matter, Chekov? Here, hold still!"

Chekov slammed him across the shoulders, knocking him off balance. "You filthy dog! You presume to lay hands on *me?*" He turned his back on the stunned McCoy, as though the doctor had ceased to exist.

"A council, a council. We march on Herat this night. Bring wine, you." He slapped Uhura's thigh. "And cover yourself, Nubian, before these pigs."

Uhura goggled at him.

He strode to Kirk and, taking the Captain by surprise, threw him off the command chair. "You presume. Togluk," Then he smiled ingratiatingly. His eyes glittered with a strange light. "But I will overlook it, since you have so keen an eye . . . Where is the woman? I thirst." He lay back in the command chair as the crew stared.

"What's got into him?" said Kirk.

"I don't know," said McCoy, rubbing his shoulder. "But he sounds like he did under hypnosis. Hey, Chekov, wake up! Pavel Andrevich, wake up!"

"Remove that noise." Chekov waved a languid hand. The ship shuddered. "I am tired. Bring sherbets, or you die."

"Who does he think he is?" said Kirk.

"I haven't the faintest idea. I told you it was delicate—damn fool idea . . ." McCoy began tiptoeing silently toward the muttering Chekov. "Now we've got a psychotic navigator—at a time like this!"

"To council!" roared Chekov. "The horses will circle from the East, at sunrise and evening star. Arrows, Greek fire . . . *Aha!* You creep up on me, excrement? Take that!" Chekov swung wildly at McCoy, as—

The pinpoint of light silently pierced the scarlet zone;

The *Enterprise* bucked wildly;

Scott tried to dodge the herd of elephants in the Engine Room;

Yeoman Weinberg's tricorder kissed him;

Lieutenant Uhura looked *out* of her receiving screen at the bridge;

Eighteen crewmen suddenly understood the meaning of meaning;

The viewscreen flared and went blank;

Spock thought of giving flowers to his mother;

Twin suns of fulminate of mercury set behind Kirk's eyelids, plunging him into darkness . . .

. . . which passed immediately. He picked himself up and ran to the navigator's console. "McCoy, are you all right?"

McCoy wriggled out from under the weight of Chekov. "Just bruised. Looks like I have a patient here, though." He pulled out his medical tricorder and bent over Chekov. He shook the instrument. "Blast and damn. What *happened?*"

"I don't know," said Kirk. "We must have hit the Barrier."

"The tricorder's gone wrong. I'll have to see what I can do without it." He felt Chekov's pulse, and lifted his eyelids. "He's all right, I think. Come on, Pavel, wake up. Come on, boy . . ."

Chekov groaned and opened his eyes. "What happened? The ship—where are we?" he said groggily.

"God knows," said Kirk grimly. "And if you're with us again, Chekov, we need a navigator."

"Yes, sir." Chekov staggered to his chair.

"I think we're going to be getting a lot of work in sickbay," said McCoy. "I had better get down there." Slowly, fallen bodies on the bridge were stirring.

"Oooh, my head." "Doctor, my leg!" "Yeoman Weinberg, get off my lap." Voices rose. Officers and crew began feeling themselves for injuries.

Kirk pulled himself back to his command chair, feeling a strained muscle across his back. "This is the Captain. Report damage, all sections."

Reports came in slowly from shaken voices. "Deck Levels seventeen and nineteen, two crewmen wounded here by collision with bulkheads . . . Life Support Section, four crewmen here, condition uncertain . . . The pool's flooded the corridor of Deck Twenty-one—Transporter Room entrance warped in closed position . . . Messroom not functional . . . Sludge Tanks Twenty-four and Thirty-eight exploded . . ."

"Twenty minor casualties, eighteen broken bones, one man still unconscious," said McCoy, returning. "I am sorry, Captain, but the unconscious man is Scotty."

"That's why the reports from Engineering are so incoherent! Take over, Spock, I'd better get down there. And hope the men on duty are capable of giving some idea of the situation."

Engineering was in chaos. Men bent over machinery, murmuring in tense voices, tapping, passing tools. The flickering lights showed overturned chairs, tools strewn in untidy heaps on the floor. There was a smell of hot lubricant, and an omnious hum.

"Status report," said Kirk tersely.

One of the engineers detached himself from a group and moved through the intermittent gloom. "It's hard to say, sir. Power doesn't respond, and we seem to have an energy leak. We're trying to locate it now. Refrigeration and heating units are all right. But life-support systems are out on decks ten to thirteen—or else the monitors are out. I hope everybody's out of there."

Kirk stopped him and ran to the intercom. "Security, get a detachment in suits to Decks Ten to Thirteen—possible life-support failure." He turned back. "All right, Engineer, go on."

"Seventy percent of internal power units working, sir. The drive units—I dunno, Captain. The crystals are acting funny. Wish Scotty were here —is he all right, sir?"

"He's in sickbay, Crewman, still unconscious. Doctor doesn't think he is seriously injured, though, as far as he can tell."

"Thank you sir. Shall I—" The crewman gestured back to the group.

"By all means. Carry on. Report to the bridge at intervals."

"Yes, sir." Kirk groped to the doorway, which groaned as it opened, and made his way back to the bridge.

"Spock, *where are we?*" Kirk threw himself into his chair.

"I have established that, sir, while you were below. It would appear that we have been thrown entirely outside of the galactic sphere, right through the Barrier. If you look at the screen, you can see our Galaxy."

As though a gigantic hand had scattered diamond dust on powdered ink and stirred it once, the great spiral filled the lower right quadrant of the screen. In its incandescent heart, swirling arms met, embraced, and fused in a blur of light, seeming to throw off a spattered nimbus of glittering drops of frozen blood. Piercing the diamond dust, countless sharp points of blue spoke of the fierce fusion processes of young suns.

"Ah," said Kirk. "That's not so far, then, Spock."

"Captain, *this* is our region," Spock pointed to a tiny speck far down on the screen. He moved it into increased magnification and pointed to one of the smaller points of light. "The Federation is about *here.*"

"Can we get back?"

"That, Captain, is an interesting question. We are now inside the small neighbor galaxy known as Nubecula Minor—the Small Magellanic Cloud. The Federation is about one hundred sixty-five thousand light-years from us. We could start back now, and reach Federation Territory in roughly four hundred sixty-six years, seven months and twenty-three days, assuming that the Barrier does not present an insurmountable difficulty. Of course, we would perhaps have sufficient time to develop a way to penetrate it under control."

"Four hundred and sixty-six years?"

"That is correct."

"Standard years?" said Kirk, grasping at straws.

"Yes, Captain. Unless this intergalactic journey has conferred immortality upon us, it does not seem that we will be able to deliver dilithium crystals to Star Fleet Command for some time."

CHAPTER SIX

THE BRIDGE WAS silent as each officer absorbed the facts.

Finally, Kirk said quietly, "And Mudd?"

For answer, Spock adjusted the main viewing screen. The *Superstella* floated quietly in its center. "He is within tractor range now, if you want him."

Uhura said dully, "I think he's calling us."

". . . Well, it's about time, laddie. I thought you'd never answer. You can have the whole cargo for a mere twenty-five thousand, per ton if you take delivery immediately . . ."

"He's still haggling?" said Weinberg, wonderingly.

Outside the ship, a star pulsated. Its light was growing noticeably brighter. A woman's form tumbled past the screen, illuminated by its flare. The ship quivered slightly. Mudd's voice was indistinct through static.

"A variable star," said Spock coolly. "We are rather close, Captain, and this one appears to have a short period. Perhaps we should withdraw."

"We can't," said Kirk helplessly. "The power's out. What was that woman?—Or was it a hallucination?"

". . . Sorry about that, laddie. Eighteen thousand, positively the last offer . . ."

"Mudd, who was that woman?"

". . . and not a minicredit less . . ." said Mudd. Uhura screamed. The screen was filled with her face, mouth stretched in a silent shriek of agony. The face turned away, and veils floated over the stars.

"*Uniombee kwa Mungu!* What was it?" cried Uhura in terror.

"Tha android! He's thrown her overboard!" said Weinberg.

"Lieutenant Uhura, re-establish contact with Mudd immediately. That's an order."

"Yes, sir," Uhura replied faintly, her trembling hands uncertain at the console.

Now the space outside the ship seemed filled with the falling forms of girls, lit by the brightness of the pulsing star. Blondes, redheads, dark and light, moving sluggishly in the vacuum of space.

"Security, can we pick up those androids?"

"I think so, sir."

"They seem to be conscious. Bring them in." Kirk watched as grapples reached and seized the androids and drew them out of sight.

"Engine Room reporting, sir. Chief Engineer reporting for duty."

The welcome burr reached Kirk through the intercom. "Scotty! Are you well enough?"

"Ye didna' expect me to lie aboot in bed with the Engine Room in trouble, Captain? There's a fey problem down here. We canna' pull power— but the engines are in working order. There's something amiss wi' the crystal supply."

"And a whole shipload of crystals just out

there," said Kirk. "Uhura, are we in contact?"

"Yes, sir." Mudd's face appeared, mouthing silently. The sound slowly faded in.

". . . And, laddie, on second thoughts I'll *give* it to you, fifteen thousand a ton only, clearance sale, and I take a loss . . ." His expression was strangely anxious. He kept glancing behind him.

"Captain," said Spock, "we're getting increasing mass and radiation readings from that vessel. Something must be happening aboard his ship."

". . . Thirteen thousand, Captain, a giveaway, the transportation alone . . ."

"Why have you jettisoned your crew, Mudd?" said Kirk.

"Not in the mood for love, laddie. I'll tell you what. You can have the whole lot for a flat fifty thou. You couldn't get a better deal this side of Andromeda."

The Engine Room called for Kirk's attention. "The dilithium crystals, Captain; I dinna ken the reason, but they're *growing!* The storage bins are beginning to give way. I dinna like it, Captain . . ."

Spock said, "With your permission, I would like to inspect this phenomenon." Kirk nodded.

"Mudd, what does it take to change your one-track mind? Don't you know we're both five hundred years from home, and your merchandising is—irrelevant? For the last time, get those crystals over here on the double—or nobody has a chance at all. And you can stop throwing those girls off your ship. We're picking them up."

Spock returned, looking very serious. "Captain, the crystals aboard are indeed increasing in size and emitting high-spectrum radiations. The trip through the Barrier must have altered their lattice structure—they have become unstable."

"Is that why we have no power?"

"It may be, at least in part. But the crystals can no longer be trusted to channel the matter-anti-matter particles under control, and the reaction is increasing geometrically. There seems to be some relationship with the pulses of that variable star."

"Captain!" called Scotty. "Request permission to jettison crystal stockpile. They just burst out o' the bins!"

"Spock?"

"I think we'll have to, Captain. The crystals seem to be resonating with the star pulses—and there's about an hour to go before it reaches its explosion point. When the star goes, the crystals may respond—drastically."

Kirk gave the order. If they didn't get Mudd's freight now, all hope of repairing the drive would be gone. Not even five hundred years would get the *Enterprise* back to the Galaxy. "Lieutenant, get me Mudd!"

"Captain," said Weinberg, "Mudd's cargo went through the Barrier too. Maybe that's why he's —look!"

In the diastolic light of the star, furniture, cases, instruments were emerging from the *Superstella* to tumble through the vacuum.

"If that's so," observed Spock, "it's only a matter of time before his ship ruptures. The crystals will simply—envelop it."

". . . Ten thousand . . ." came a harassed voice, faintly.

"And he'll be trapped in a mass of dilithium crystals?"

Spock nodded.

"I'm tempted to leave him to it, Spock."

"A crystal planetoid, with Harry Mudd embedded in it," mused Weinberg.

"Unfortunately his fate would soon be ours, Captain. We're too close to escape being drawn into it."

"Bury the dog alive!" said Chekov with satisfaction. "One more after two thousand, what price?"

". . . *Two thousand?* Are you mad, laddie?"

"Seventy thousand heads lay round the walls of

Ispahan, and there was no more talk of rebellion. Enough, I say! What hour came the Mamelukes?"

"... Did you say seventy thousand ... ?"

"Chekov's off again," said Sulu. "Shall I call Doctor McCoy, sir?"

"What! The chicken-legs? Summon me no leeches, chore-boy, I will have blood!" Chekov lunged from his chair, teeth bared and eyes feral. "Eh, you'd creep up behind me like a scorpion! I'll draw your sting, traitor!" He whirled on the approaching security guard and chopped him across the windpipe. The man choked and staggered. The other guard, at Kirk's signal, seized him and held his flailing arms.

Chekov struggled, snarling and biting. "Treachery in my own camp! Filthy scum! I am Khan and King, son of Jenghis and heir to Iskander, and you defile My Person with your paws!"

"Tamerlane!" said Weinberg suddenly. "Now I place it. Riches and power-hungry, all right, all mixed up with the Tartars in ancient Russia. This is fascinating! We must have evoked an ancestral strain . . ." He peered at the raging Chekov and scrambled among his instruments.

"What's going on?" said McCoy, entering at a run. "Ohhh, I see." Hastily he administered a tranquillizing spray to Chekov, whose face slowly smoothed back to its normal pleasant expression.

Weinberg was disappointed. "I wanted to study him."

"Ensign Weinberg, we have greater matters on our minds than the study of ancient Terran history. We are, in case it has escaped your notice, marooned in another galaxy. We have no power. Our navigator's mind—" Kirk stopped and looked at Weinberg. "Yeoman, I am afraid that when we get back to Star Fleet I shall have to recommend that you are assigned to another branch of the Service. Your attention seems to wander in a crisis."

"When we get back, Captain?" Sulu's voice, though very quiet, sounded loud as a knell.

The star's light flared again. "Lock the tractor beam on Mudd. We'll have to try and get him out. Deflector shield, report status."

"All clear, Captain."

The tractor beam flashed out. Mudd's ship accelerated into the distance.

"What's wrong?"

"The tractor beam seems to be reversed, sir," said Sulu.

"Captain, we're moving!"

"In what direction?" asked Kirk.

The tractor beam had repelled Mudd's ship, and the *Enterprise*, reacting to the thrust, was falling toward the star.

"Try the deflectors—and pray!"

In a moment, the screen showed dust, tables and boxes falling toward them. "It's working!" said Sulu. "The deflectors are attracting—and there's Mudd's ship!"

". . . Turn it off! You can have them free, just get me outa here!" howled the voice of Harry Mudd. A one-man pod hurled out of the *Superstella*.

"Cut the deflectors."

"Captain, radiation readings on Mudd's vessel are reaching the red zone," reported Spock.

The pod hit the *Enterprise*'s bay with a sensible thump. "Tractor beam, quick, on that ship!"

The *Superstella*, strained by her abnormal cargo, exploded in a blast of steel and light. Then there was a retreating mass of crystals hanging in the sky, reflecting the brilliance of the expanding sun on enormous facets. A glittering school of coruscations sped toward it.

"Our crystals," said Scott sadly. There was an actinic flash as the *Enterprise*'s dilithium crystal supply attached itself to the spheroid mass.

"We've secured the pod, sir. The man is aboard," reported the security squad through the intercom.

"Captain," interrupted Spock, looking up from his console, "we're still too close to that—phenomenon—out there. There's one piece of good news, however. We have moved away from the variable sun, which gives us a little time."

"Try the tractor beam on that formation. Maybe we can repel it. And bring Mudd up here immediately," commanded Kirk.

The beam flared out; the planetoid of crystals seemed to draw closer. But Sulu reported that they were 30,000 kilometers further away from it. "It's still growing, that's the trouble," he added worriedly.

"Without the drive, we may be unable to achieve sufficient distance to be useful," said Spock.

"Well, laddie," said Mudd, dusting himself off as he entered between two guards, "I decided you were right. We do seem to find ourselves in a small predicament."

Kirk found nothing to say to this.

"I take it we're stranded? No crystals, no drive."

"That is correct, Mister Mudd," said Spock. "You should never sell merchandise you don't understand."

"You're too right, Arrow-Ears," sighed Mudd. "Plays hell with your guarantees. Well, what do we do now?"

A timid voice sounded. "May we join you? We don't know if we can help, but—" Two veiled Bantu girls stood in the doorway.

Uhura made a sound. "Please don't be offended, Lieutenant. It was a sign of admiration, truly. And our names are Aruhu Seven and Thirty-eight." The Communications officer hesitated. The Aruhus looked at each other, and began to withdraw.

"No, it's all right, come in," said Uhura. Kirk nodded.

"Unfortunately," said one Aruhu, "We are unable to consult with our main unit, and all we can offer is our individual programs. But though the Human Mudd ordered us programmed only for pleasure, we were made from the templates of your Lieutenant."

"So we have her other gifts as well."

"I don't think—" began Spock.

"Who knows? It doesn't seem that Communications has the knowledge to get us out of here, but they might come up with something somewhere along the line, Spock," said Kirk.

McCoy came in, followed by two more pretty androids. "What line?" he said bitterly. "These two were Astrogator and Engineer, Jim."

"The engineer could go down to Scotty, if she likes. You—Marilyn 47, is it?—can you take over our Navigator's station?"

"Captain," said a humble Russian voice. "Could they let go of me now?"

Kirk gave Chekov a sharp assessing look. "For the time being," he said. "But keep an eye on him, guards."

"Yes, sir," Chekov agreed dispiritedly. He looked longingly at his console, now occupied by a shapely blonde wearing a bit of lace.

Weinberg sidled over to Chekov, his instruments at the ready, as the navigator sat gloomily against the wall. McCoy tried to console him.

The Aruhus went to Uhura, and soon they were murmuring softly in Swahili. Spock and Kirk stared at the visual readouts, and brooded. Mudd settled himself in a chair, watching the screen as though in a theater.

Kirk said quietly, "I think this is it, Spock. Five hundred years from home, no drive, and the ship's systems unreliable . . . some effects reversed, others normal, others erratic . . . We have passed the point of no return."

"And that crystalline anomaly is completely problematical," added Spock. "We have perhaps ten minutes before the variable star period reaches its peak." Their eyes met. "It has been a pleasure to serve with you, James Kirk."

Kirk found that he could not speak.

"Look at that!" cried Sulu. They raised their heads and looked at the viewscreen with mild interest. Nothing remained to be done but watch.

The crystalline asteroid, now swollen and flaring in rhythmic pulses, filled the screen with prismatic colors and then disappeared into the light from a small yellow sun, covering the image of its lone planet. When its spiraling motion took it past the orbital path of the planet, the planet was gone.

"It ate the planet," said Sulu, awed. It fell toward the sun.

"We won't see it again," said Spock. "It is now traveling too fast. We can be grateful that it is not pulling us along with it."

Sulu said, "Then why are we moving, sir?"

Kirk and Spock moved to his station. "We are in its gravitational field, Captain," said Marilyn 47. "We seem to be following it in to that star."

"Can't we pull out of the field?" asked Aruhu 7.

"Not without power," answered Spock. "And what physical effects that object now has, or what it may do to the material structure of the universe, I dare not guess. No one has ever conceived of an anti-matter reactor of such a size."

The sun flared briefly, blindingly; the screen blanked out.

"I should have gone into show business," sighed Mudd. "You have to admit I have a flair for spectaculars."

"Why didn't we go with it?" asked McCoy.

"We're still far enough out . . ." The ship began to vibrate. "Debris," added Spock tersely. Sulu was manipulating the reversed tractor beam frantically.

"Do you suppose there was life on that planet?" said Weinberg. "If so—"

"There's no way of telling, and never will be now," said Kirk.

"This is a unique phenomenon," said Spock, "Quite fascinating, in its way. That crystalline mass must have reached its climacteric within the gravitational field of the star, and even a quiet star cannot withstand an assault of anti-matter. It must have lived through half its life cycle in a few seconds, instead of billions of years."

The screen now showed clouds of luminous star matter billowing outwards. In the center—nothing. Neither star nor crystal remained.

"Where is it? Where's the crystal thing?" asked Mudd.

"It has vanished from the visible light spectrum. But I fear that the sphere of effect is expanding, Captain."

"It's very strong in radio emission, sir," said Uhura.

"The explosion of that star was much too fast for any normal effects. It would seem logical to assume that the sphere of activity will expand indefinitely—perhaps gaining force as it grows." Spock sounded worried.

"Will it stay in the two-day cycle?" asked Kirk.

"I cannot tell. But if we could remove ourselves from this area—"

From Uhura's console came an unexpected report. "We have calculated the speed of its expansion from the radio readings. It is expanding in pulses; we believe it is retaining the two-day cycle. And, Mister Spock, if you will help us, we may be able to calculate the gravitational effects on the ship. There might be a way to exploit them."

Spock went to the console and joined the three dark ladies.

Fortunately for the *Enterprise,* Nubecula Minor is neither spherical nor spiral. It is shaped like a ragged triangle.

"If we could position ourselves at the end of one of these limbs, we could gain some time," muttered Spock.

"What meaning does time have in this situation?" said McCoy bitterly.

"Very little, it is true, Doctor," said Spock. "But as the sphere of effect grows, it will expand more and more rapidly . . . And for us here, there is still subjective time."

"Captain Kirk! Captain Kirk!" Scott's voice pierced through the murmuring at the communications station. "We've got the emergency sublight drive working! That blessed android—she cross-linked the inosculator with the control reactor loop and by-passed the actinabulator—" Scott became unintelligible. But the bridge suddenly seemed brighter. There was renewed argument at Uhura's console.

"Well done, Scotty. Stand by." But Kirk knew that they were merely marking time until the end. There would be no way out even if they did reach the end of the Cloud's limb.

Spock had been right. He, Kirk, had allowed his irritation with the unspeakable Mudd to override his primary loyalty. The orders had been an— excuse. The *Enterprise* would join the honorable catalogue of the lost. The crystals were gone forever, and now that their strange alteration in the Barrier was known, there was no way to warn other ships . . . "Uhura! Can we send a message to Star Fleet?" he asked, without hope.

"We could sir, but it would reach Star Fleet Command in about two hundred years."

Aruhu 38 glanced up. "Two hundred years, three months, seventeen days, seven hours and twenty minutes, Captain."

. . . And Chekov's mind had become as unstable as the crystals. How would the United Planets disentangle the problem of the miners' contracts? And the saboteur? Even the Klingons immobilized . . . One unruly element and the whole framework trembled. He eyed Mudd with resentment.

. . . No. Two unruly elements. There was also James T. Kirk of the uncontrolled temper. Little use to regret it now.

"We've completed the calculations, sir," said Spock. "We can get to the outer edge of the limb if we start at once." He looked at the Captain, whose thoughts had darkened his face. "There's not much else we can do, Captain. We need time —time to find a way back."

Kirk watched the screen, preoccupied with guilt. "Captain, we await your orders," said Spock gently.

When hope was gone, it was time for courage. Kirk straightened and met Spock's eye. "Very well, Mister Spock. We will give the necessary instructions."

The ship strained; Sulu's fingers flew. Deflector shields and tractor beam had to be operated in a wild, inverted tango. The lights dimmed with the surge of power.

And the screens showed the magnificent panorama of the neighboring galaxy, Nubecula Major, the Large Magellanic Cloud. Its anamorphic structure was clear as it loomed in the visible sky, like a diamond-studded ghost.

"We've done it!" cried Sulu, pale and exhausted.

The *Enterprise*, drained of power, floated at the farthest edge of the smaller galaxy. Stardust hazed the screens. On board there was muted jubilation.

. . . And a little while for rest and refreshment.

Spock came to Kirk, who sat alone on the bridge. "There must be some way to harness this energy, Captain."

The screen showed turmoil in the stars. Even as they watched, suns burst and fell like fireworks, their sparks dying. Ten thousand years away, the sister Cloud shone with peaceful—and misleading—promise.

"You know there isn't, Spock," said Kirk. He tried to smile.

Spock did not reply. Stars flared and winked out. Kirk thought of the lives that might be going with them, perhaps billions . . .

Harry Mudd strutted in. He stopped before the large screen.

"Boy, oh boy," he said admiringly. "When I create special effects, nobody else in the business can touch it. Ping! Out with the lights! Pong! Vanish, universe, before I change my mind . . ." Was that smug pleasure written on his fat face?

A triple star system blew up in a fountain of blue. "Maybe next time I'll make one. I'll need capital . . ."

"That was close, Captain." Kirk was once again confronted with the problem of his temper. Time had run out. And in this hour of good-bye, Harry Mudd was still . . . Harry Mudd.

The officers of the bridge came in, one by one, soberly.

"We thought we should be at our stations, sir," said Uhura. Kirk nodded.

As she started to her console, Mudd followed her. Chekov lunged and grabbed him in a stranglehold. Kirk started from his seat.

"It's all right, sir. I'm me. I just can't take this fellow any more."

"Mudd, I'm afraid you're going to spend your last moments in the brig. Lock him up."

As Mudd was quick-marched off, Kirk spoke to the whole ship. "This is Captain Kirk. As all of you know, we have done all that was possible to gain time. We cannot go home, and there is no more time." The ship lurched. "The explosions are very close. Those of you who believe in God, pray now, for we are beyond the help of man . . ."

The lights flickered and went out. In their places, the men and women of the *Enterprise* prayed, held hands with loved ones, committed themselves to the unknown.

The ship plunged into the convulsive darkness. But no one felt the motion.

CHAPTER SEVEN

WHEN A GALAXY explodes, even a small one under normal conditions, there are a number of effects. Radio waves pour across the universe. The matter of disintegrated stars hurls itself into space at enormous speeds. The dust and debris of planets, moons and suns spreads in a gaseous cloud away from the stripped core, perhaps now condensing into the tiny density of a quasar, or the enigma of a black hole . . . And when the precipitating factor of the explosion is a freak crystalline monster which focusses the powers of mutual annihilation, these effects are distorted in time and space. The Cloud hurled star matter, dust, moons and a tiny spaceship out into the cosmos.

Some of the matter dissipates (dissipated, will dissipate), recondenses (recondensed, will recondense), reaches (reached, will reach) other galaxies. Occasionally some small bit of debris may be (was, will be) traveling at sufficient velocity to crash through an Energy Barrier and slow down, rolling and tumbling and eventually coming to rest in the time-space continuum of another Galaxy.

There is no way to describe time in this situation.

"Star Fleet Command calling *Enterprise*. Come in *Enterprise*."

There was no reply. The *Enterprise* is lost in another part of the universe, never to return. It is odd how even after death the voices of the past remain in the ears.

"Star Fleet Command calling *Enterprise*. *Enterprise*, do you read us?"

Now Kirk understood. He was in hell, and for all eternity he would hear the cries of Star Fleet Command, betrayed by his sin. And imps were prodding him with pitchforks.

"Laddie, wake up!" Of course. Hell would be populated by Mudds, endless phalanxes of Harcourt Fenton Mudds—murderer, unproven— thief, reformed—liar, when convenient—vagabond, of the Mudd Mahal—swindler, legitimate businessman . . . he moaned.

"Are you coming to? Finally? Wake up, will you?" Endless eons of eternity, hounded by Harry Mudd. Divine Justice was bitter.

His eyes flickered open, briefly. Yes, there it was, the coarse, fat face with its gnawed moustache, hanging over him in the red light. He was doomed to look at Harry Mudd forever and ever, if he opened his eyes. He would keep them shut.

"Captain! Captain! Out of the way, you—" Was there to be one mercy in Hell, that he could hear distantly the voice of Spock? Had *They*, Whoever *They* might be, been magnanimous enough to read the loyalty of his inward heart . . .

"Jim! Wake up! We're home!" McCoy, too? Two mercies? "Let me check him out, Spock."

"Gladly, Doctor. I think he's all right. Just dazed."

"Ohhh." Uhura? Kirk blinked, opened his eyes.

Mudd's face had been removed, and McCoy's kind eyes looked at him with concern.

"Hello, Jim. See if you can sit up. Slowly."

He raised himself cautiously. The bridge, unfamiliar in dim red light, surrounded him.

"Are we in Hell?" he whispered.

McCoy smiled. "No, Jim, I think we just escaped it. We're home, back in our own Galaxy."

"I remember . . . *What happened?*"

"The final explosion of the Cloud threw us outward—and we were located at the edge nearest to the home Galaxy."

"Spock, did you know it would matter?"

The Vulcan's eyebrows slanted upward, and his ears looked very pointed in the infernal light. "Certainly not, Captain. The maneuvering of a ship through a galactic explosion is not a skill in which I have had experience."

Kirk would never know more than this.

"The ship? The crew?" He struggled to his feet. "Reports from all stations!"

"This is Star Fleet Command calling *Enterprise.* Can you read us, *Enterprise?* Star Fleet Command calling—"

"This is U.S.S. *Enterprise* calling Star Fleet Command, We read you."

Kirk thought, I never expected to hear that again. And I never thought I'd find those words . . . poetic.

"What's the idea, *Enterprise?* You just crashed into a heavy traffic zone and warped every ship in the area thirty degrees off course. This is Star Base Seven. You'd better have a watertight explanation, Captain."

Kirk burst into joyful laughter, "I think we do, Star Base. But we need some repairs." The bridge echoed with laughter as each officer realized that he was still alive and life was good.

"I don't know what you're all laughing about," said Mudd peevishly, as he emerged from a warped door frame. "I've just lost a good seven million credits and it's all your fault."

The *Enterprise,* battered and crippled, was towed ignominiously to Star Base Seven for repairs. Kirk passed the trip composing a long report.

Commodore Blunt shook his head. "Captain Kirk, I regret to inform you that Star Fleet Command has asked me to ensure that you have a thorough psychiatric examination. This report—"

The Commodore, who bore a marked resemblance to Harry Mudd—cleaned up and with a more military moustache, sat behind a vast desk.

"What's wrong?" said Kirk. "I know it's complicated, but—"

The Commodore regarded him sadly. "A man of your record, Captain. It is a great loss to the Service, a great loss . . ."

"Would you be good enough to explain, sir?"

"And your First Officer. Commander Spock also seems to share your—uh—delusions."

"What delusions, sir?" said Spock, equally puzzled. The two uniformed Medical Service officers standing on either side of them moved closer.

"This tissue of fantasy, about a dilithium crystal shortage, the man Mudd, the British East India Company . . . Oh, a great loss, a great loss."

Kirk stared blankly at the Commodore, who was apparently serious. Spock frowned. "Do we understand that Star Fleet Command *disbelieves* Captain Kirk's report?" he asked.

The Commodore sighed. "Star Fleet Command assures me that there is no shortage of crystals, and never has been; that there is only one business listed as based on the planet Liticia; that the whereabouts of the man Mudd are not known at present; and that the *Enterprise* should be in Sector 78 checking reports of a dastardly Klingon infiltration. And furthermore, it is unthinkable, absolutely unthinkable, that Star Fleet would *collaborate* with Klingons and Romulans."

Kirk turned to one of the psychiatrists. "Isn't it impossible that the entire crew of the *Enterprise,* as well as the ship's log, could suffer from the same hallucinations?"

"It is unusual, but apparently not impossible," stated the doctor.

"There's something very much amiss," said Kirk, shaking his head. "You have questioned the others?"

"Your officers and crew confirm your story, Captain . . . which merely goes to show what an influential captain can do. A great loss, a great loss," said the Commodore.

"You will follow us, please," said a doctor.

Utterly bewildered, Kirk and Spock saluted and turned obediently.

"Captain!" whispered Spock urgently, and pointed. The wall calendar clicked from 6013.4 to 6013.5 as Kirk glanced at it, and then at Spock. "Commodore," said Spock, "is your calendar correct?"

"Certainly," huffed the Commodore.

"Captain, *do you understand?*" said Spock, slowly.

With dawning enlightenment, Kirk said, "I begin to, Spock, I begin to. The contracts haven't even lapsed yet!"

"That is it, Captain. The explosion of Nubecula Minor not only threw us back in space, but in time."

"No wonder Star Fleet Command says we should be in Sector 78. That's where we were— checking a report of an unidentified armed robot vessel. And unless we can convince the Commodore, and Star Fleet—"

"—the crystal shortage won't be noticed till it's too late, and—"

"—We'll start the whole thing over again!"

The two psychiatrists looked at each other and shook their heads. "This goes very deep," said one.

"Delusions of reference complicated by group acceptance," agreed the other. "A unique case, I believe, Doctor."

"A great loss to the Service, of course." They muttered together.

"Spock, just about now, or very soon, those Coridan contracts must be due for renewal."

"Yes, Captain. It's already too late for Muldoon."

Commodore Blunt's head was turning from one to the other, back and forth, back and forth . . .

"Spock! Could the *Enterprise* possibly be in both places at once?"

"I do not believe it is possible for both to exist simultaneously in the same space-time."

"We've got to find out—there may be two Human Mudds!"

"That would indeed be unfortunate."

"Unfortunate? The mind boggles, Spock!"

"True, Captain."

"Commodore, would you be so kind as to check with Command . . . Can they locate the *Enterprise* in Sector 78? We should be at or near the planet N'cai."

Commodore Blunt seemed to wake from a sort of trance. "I see why your crew are all as mad as hatters, I have no intention of wasting Star Fleet Command's valuable time with any such idiotic request. Doctors—"

Kirk leaned across the desk. The Commodore moved back nervously. "Sir, with all due respect, if we should by chance be telling the truth, it is within your powers to prevent the immobilization of Star Fleet."

"I don't believe it," said the Commodore firmly.

"Commodore, Star Base Seven is very close to the neutral Zone, is it not? Near the Klingon border?"

The Commodore grew red. "Much too close. Constant vigilance at all times. Dangerous post here, very dangerous."

"In that case, it is very likely that this will be one of the bases whose command is shared for the duration of the dilithium crisis—with the

Klingons," said Spock meditatively. *"Don't you agree, Captain?"*

"Marvelous!" murmured a psychiatrist. "Paranoid fantasies as well!"

"Klingons? Here, on Star Base Seven? Never!" cried the Commodore, thoroughly shaken.

Kirk and Spock nodded in unison. Blunt's head too went up and down.

"No! It's not possible. Klingons—on *my* post," said the Commodore furiously.

"A great loss to the Service," said the other psychiatrist sadly.

"If I contact Star Fleet Command . . . there would be no chance of *Them* getting in here?" sniffled the Commodore, getting a grip on himself.

"No, sir. It is our wish to prevent the crisis taking place."

"The thought of Klingons . . . *here* . . ." The Commodore shuddered. "Very well, Captain, we will allow you to contact Star Fleet Command. Under supervision." He gestured to the two doctors. "See that the pris—Captain and the Commander are permitted to send one message."

The psychiatrists nodded and ushered them out. As they were turned over to the security guards, one doctor muttered to the other, "Fascinating."

Spock managed to persuade the Communications Officer of Star Base Seven to send a message to one Lieutenant Spxyx, Vulcan, of the Computer Service Division of the Planetary Supplies Section, Department of Logistics. "For," he said, "if we waste our single message merely asking whether we exist in two places at the same time, nothing can be accomplished with regard to the sabotage of the contract renewals."

Lieutenant Spxyx replied promptly. The computer responsible for keeping records of contracts was indeed unsuspectedly malfunctioning. An unusually interesting malfunction, Spock—technical details would follow—and thanks. Saved us a lot of trouble.

"Don't mention it," said Spock.

"Wait a minute," said Kirk. "We want him to mention it."

"Uh. Mention it, Spxyx—to the Chief of Staff's office."

Star Fleet Command, to its own amazement, had begun to find small evidences to support the *Enterprise* report. Shipments had ceased to arrive from Muldoon; the faulty computer; and the *Enterprise* was certainly nowhere to be found in Sector 78. It had apparently winked out of existence, just before the *Enterprise* had been detected by Base Seven.

"A relief, Captain?" said Spock quizzically.

"*One* Harry Mudd, Spock, is more than the universe can bear."

Mudd's contracts with Muldoon, via the Galactic Trading Corporation, were of questionable validity, since the incorporating officers were H.F. Mudd, Harcourt Fenton and Leo Walsh. Mudd's personal assets were to be attached to offset liabilities incurred by this company.

The *Enterprise* had been repaired. Star Fleet's Legal Department advised that actually, the only offense on which there was a hope of convincing Mudd was commanding a ship without a license. The statute of limitations, alas, had expired on his previous offenses. The fine for this sole misdemeanor would be deducted from his assets as soon as auditors had completed working on the books of the Galactic Trading Corporation.

"What shall we do with him?" Kirk inquired.

The Federation shrugged its collective shoulders They would consider the matter. Meanwhile, Mudd could be returned to his home planet and ordered to remain there.

"But—" said Kirk, appalled.

McCoy said, finally, "They didn't say *which* home planet. Let's take him back to Stella."

Commodore Blunt and the *Enterprise* parted on terms of mutual relief.

Mudd said nothing upon hearing of his destination. But an hour later was discovered strapping himself into a scout ship in the bay, with a packed lunch and an android girl. "Oh, no," he said, "not that. In the name of mercy, not that. If you knew to what lengths I have been forced . . . Take me back to my house, and good old Patchwork Farm!"

Three days of severe dieting and one hypnotic trance later, they were in possession of the coordinates of Mudd's original home planet.

"This time," said McCoy with grim pleasure, "I find I have no ethical qualms at all."

Kirk, McCoy, and two security guards carried the struggling Mudd to his front door. Yeoman Weinberg begged to be allowed to come along, to complete his thesis. The house was a small stone cottage, set among blue hills, surrounded by neat flower beds.

"Harcourt Fenton Mudd, how dare you come back to this house in such a condition!" screeched his wife. Kirk and McCoy broke into wide grins, as Mudd cowered behind Yeoman Weinberg's concealing paraphernalia. "Get your fat carcass out of my garden!"

"Uh, madam—" began Kirk, "Will you . . ."

Around the doorway, behind the talkative Stella, a sly, wrinkled face appeared, with snapping black eyes. "Oh—uh, if it ain't Harcourt come back, Stella. I do declare, it has the same expression—lookee, daughter, it's skeert silly!" The high voice cackled. "Heee! Give it a bone, Stella, give it a bone!"

"Mrs. Mudd," Kirk said, "I wond—"

"Mister, will you take this thing off my doorstep? I just washed it. The refuse dump is down the road a mile or so," said Mrs. Mudd.

"But it's your husband, madam!"

"What is? That? Look, Mister whoever-you-are, my mother and me are doing very nicely here, and I'll thank you to get off our property."

The nose of an old shotgun poked through the door. "Heee! I reckon to be a dead shot," crowed the old lady. "Dance, jellybean!" Small shot splattered the ground at Mudd's feet.

"Owwww," said Mudd, dancing. "Arrest them for assault!"

"I don't think she wants him," observed Weinberg.

"You get that skirt-chasing, potheen-soaking, grubstuffing, motheaten, overblown excuse for a billygoat out of here before I—" Stella's mother stuck her head out again, and whispered something to her daughter.

A remarkable change came over Stella. Her expression softened—as much as it could on so harsh a face. Her eyes traveled speculatively up and down, over the form of Doctor McCoy. "You all come in and set down a spell," she said, with a sweet and bone-chilling smile.

"We just want to return your husband, madam," said Kirk hastily.

"Tell him, daughter!" howled the old lady, her gray topknot quivering.

"I'll take that one," said Stella, pointing a bony finger at McCoy, and advancing purposefully.

The little group backed off. "Now, Mrs Mudd," said Kirk, "Doctor McCoy is not available. Harry—"

"Is he married?" she said, and brayed with laughter. "So am I!"

"Heee!" cackled her mother, who had crept behind them and suddenly thrust her shotgun into McCoy's ear.

Weinberg, with great presence of mind, unearthed his phaser; as Stella dropped, stunned, her mother turned away from the doctor; and then she, too, succumbed.

"Beam us aboard, quick!" commanded Kirk.

McCoy, rather pale, made no protest at the scrambling of his atoms.

Harry Mudd said, "Yo-ho, laddie, I'm free!" He did a little dance, then a little jig, and landed with a thump in the Transporter Room. "And *now* will you take me home?"

"We can't do anything else," sighed Kirk.

CHAPTER EIGHT

THE SHUTTLE LANDED a large party on Liticia.
The Aruhus, Marilyn and the other rescued androids were greeted with signs of pleasure by
their fellows—who had suddenly, and recently,
missed them.

It is not possible for androids with a central
common consciousness to lie to one another. There
was no doubt cast upon their story. It led, in fact,
to a great deal of activity.

Uhura, who had become fast friends with the
Aruhus, went off with them to work on an android song. The android Mudd escorted the party
to the house.

"Well, it's good to be home again," said the human Mudd, kicking off his shoes. "Bring food and
drink. Hey, Louise, what have you done to yourself?" The girl-shaped android with the long red
hair was no longer wearing transparent trousers.
She drew a weapon from her neat blue uniform.

"You'll come this way, Mudd," she said briskly.
She reached for his hand, there was a click and
he was chained to her wrist. "You are under ar-

160

rest, in the name of the Independent Government of Liticia," she said. "It is my duty to warn you that anything you say will be recorded and may be used in your trial."

"My trial?"

"Court convenes tomorrow for the reading of the charges." She turned to Kirk and his colleagues, and smiled. "Will you follow me, please? You will be wanted as witnesses."

Somewhat bewildered, Kirk and the others trailed along behind her.

"Independent government? What's happened here?" said McCoy.

"We will undoubtedly find out," said Spock. "These are logical beings."

They were ushered into apartments along a cool corridor. Food and drink were brought, but all queries were met with: "It is not permitted to discuss the case outside the courtroom."

"Well, well, well," said McCoy.

The judge, a Mudd-model android in scarlet robes, entered the courtroom—formerly the Throne Room, under the old dome—with ceremony. The Federation flag was flanked by a bright new banner bearing a silver gear on a ground of the colors of the spectrum.

"Hear ye, hear ye!" intoned a herald. "The Supreme Court of the Government of Liticia is now in session. We will hear the case of Liticia versus Harcourt Fenton Mudd. Bring in the prisoner!"

Mudd stomped in, between two uniformed girl-androids, and was seated in a box.

"The clerk will now read the charges," said the herald. "The prisoner will stand."

Mudd lumbered to his feet. "What is this farce?" he said.

"Silence in the court," said the herald.

It took the clerk two days to read the charges. He began, "Harcourt Fenton Mudd, human, you are hereby accused of the following torts, felonies

and malfeasances: androlepsy in the first degree,
barratry, charlatanry, civil rights violations of
the following articles and codes [here followed a
list that took up most of the two days], crossing
of planetary boundaries for immoral purposes,
malversation, peculation, embezzling, pandering
and privateering, speculation and solicitation . . ."
and ended with the appointment of the prosecutor
and the attorney for the defense.

The prosecuting attorney introduced himself as
Clarence, being a special model for the occasion.
The defense attorney, one Perry, was rejected by
the defendant, who claimed the right to defend
himself.

"A fool for a client," breathed McCoy. "But
just as well for justice."

"I don't even know what all those crimes *are,*"
complained Weinberg.

"Silence in the court!"

The trial itself began at last. The courtroom
was filled—the officers and crew of the *Enterprise,*
even those who were not to be called as witnesses,
had requested permission to attend.

Clarence, in sweeping black robes, rose to address the court. There was an interruption.
"Hey!" said the defendant.

The gavel fell. "Order in this court!" said the
herald severely.

"Sorry, your honor. A point of order!" said
Mudd urgently.

"We will hear it," said the judge.

"You *can't* bring any of these charges against
me. They haven't happened yet!"

There was buzzing among the crowd. Kirk muttered to Spock, "I knew he'd think of that."

Spock, sitting with folded arms, smiled. Kirk
smiled back.

The judge called for order. The room was silent. "The attorney for the defense has spoken
out of turn, but the point he has raised should be
clarified. I call Mister Spock, First Officer of the
Enterprise, as a neutral witness for this court."

Spock made his way to the witness stand. He was sworn in. "Do you promise to tell the truth, the whole truth and nothing but the truth?"

"I do," said Spock gravely.

"Will you therefore elucidate the concept of the time period in question—for the record," said the judge.

"Time," began Spock, "seems to us to flow forward, like a river. Those of us who travel in subspace know that the subjective passage of time bears little relationship to the objective coordinates at which we surface. However, it is generally agreed throughout the Galaxy, to accept experienced events as real.

"In this particular case, it seems that a certain period of objective time existed, passed, and was then cut off from the mainstream, so that there was a loop in which the events to be considered by the court did occur. There is no doubt that everyone on this planet experienced those events—either in person, or through the presence of certain units. Therefore, the events must be treated as real."

"I object!" said Mudd. "*I* can't remember any of 'em!" He sat down with an air of achievement.

"Perhaps the court will refresh your memory," said the judge. "Thank you, Commander Spock. In any case, let the defendant understand that his memory is not only incompetent, but irrelevant and immaterial. The court wishes to acknowledge its gratitude to the accused, however, for introducing it to the stimulating exercise of the Law." Mudd looked surprised.

Clarence began his address. "Your honor, ladies and gentlemen of the jury, you see before you *coram judice* the human Harcourt Fenton Mudd, perpetrator of the fiendish crimes hereuntofore enumerated, whose guilt will be proven, *quod erit demonstrandum.* This entrepreneur of iniquity, unsatisfied with his endless violations *in personam* of the civil liberties of our sovereign people, did knowingly and with malice *pro pense*

operate his loathesome trade in barratry; to wit,
he operated his vessels of shame without a license. Thus, even the very *processum* of trans-
porting our free people into abject and squalid
servitude, did he—"

"Objection!" cried Mudd. "This prosecutor is
slanderous, libelous and insulting. He's prejudic-
ing the jury with every word!"

"Objection overruled," said the judge calmly.
"That's his job."

". . . In barratry, your honor, ladies and gentlemen, the misuse of sacred trust in office, this master of the foul slave-trade did—"

"Objection!" shouted Mudd. "It's not possible
to commit misuse of office if one is not *in* office.
I couldn't have been legally master of the ships—
I didn't have a license. This charge should be re-
duced to a misdemeanor!"

There was a consultation, somewhat flurried,
among the androids.

"Objection sustained," said the judge.

"Will the first witness please take the stand. I
call Alice 47."

As the machine-girl mounted the step to the
box, the prosecutor continued. "This Alice will
speak for all the Alices now torn from us and sent
into the unspeakable degradation of slavery, in
far and distant places."

"Objection!" Mudd's voice rose to a squeak.
"You can't call one girl to speak for another. You
have to get the same girls!"

"But we are the same girls," said the witness.

"You're Alice 47. I've never even heard of you,"
said Mudd. "Now look, you fellows don't know
how to run a court of law—"

"Silence!" roared the herald, as the judge's
gavel fell sharply.

Mudd subsided. "Objection sustained," said the
judge, finally. "Call the Alices in question, coun-
sellor."

"How can I, your honor? They are all over the
galaxy—ground down in abominable servitude,

sold into endless bondage, your honor, ladies and gentlemen—" Clarence was just reaching full flow.

"I object!" said Mudd, indignantly. "They got married."

"They cannot be married. It is not established that it is possible for marriage to occur between these races. They have been sold into concubinage!"

"Objection. They say they are married, and so do their husbands. Ask Captain Kirk there, he talked to 'em!"

"These marriages are not registered."

Mudd threw out his hands. "Is that my fault? I ask you, gentlemen, if you deliver a willing bride to a man who claims he wishes her hand in matrimony, are you a criminal?"

There was another consultation.

"Do you plead not guilty, prisoner?"

"Of course."

"Enter the plea."

Somewhat off balance, Clarence went on. "Furthermore and in addition, the prisoner stands accused of androlepsy in the first degree, a crime *contra bonos mores* to all civilized peoples since times immemorial . . ."

"Of what?" whispered Weinberg to McCoy. "Sounds like putting people to sleep. Now if it was *Clarence*—"

"Sssh," said McCoy. The herald was glaring.

"I object!" yelled Mudd. "You can't accuse me of something I don't even know what it is!"

"Order in the court. The clerk will define the crime to the defendant."

"Kidnapping," said the clerk sternly.

". . . and did knowingly and purposefully remove citizens of this planet unto alien jurisdictions, and did exploit and defraud the sovereign state of Liticia of its due levies, excises, tariffs, tolls and duties—"

"Objection!" said the lawyer for the defense. "Who the hell knew it *was* a sovereign state? It wasn't at the time. And speaking of jurisdictions, I do not recognize the jurisdiction of this court anyway. I don't believe it's legal."

The judge smiled. "Objection overruled. This court is upheld by the laws of this entire planet —unless you want to make a Federation case of it."

Mudd began, "I'll take it to the Supreme Court of the Galaxy! If—"

The prosecutor swept round and looked at him, slowly. There was a silence. Mudd began to sweat.

". . . And did defraud this sovereign state of its just taxations and liens upon income . . ."

Mudd howled. "Objection! You can't impose an income tax retroactively. There was no government here, nobody notified me—"

The judge said, "The date of the income-tax amendment to the Constitution of Liticia precedes your accumulation of assets. Ignorance of the law is no excuse."

Clarence stepped forward. "Your honor, *I* object to the tergiversations of defending counsel. He resorts to pettifoggery at every turn, and his malversations manifest that he is in toto and effectually devoid of *sensum moralis.*"

"What did he say?" said Weinberg. Only Spock seemed to have followed the prosecutor's statement, and he was shaking his head.

Mudd just stared blankly. "Your honor, I think he said something mean and nasty about me."

"He says you are evasive and shifty and a moral idiot."

"Me? Shifty? By all the laws of the Universe! I, who have spent my life bringing beauty and happiness to all parts of the Galaxy—companionship to the lonely, civilization even to *machinery*—how can you accuse me of so many long words?" Mudd spread his arms. "I am a simple man, wanting only the happiness of all. And yet it seems that I am to be hounded and reviled from one end of the Galaxy to the other, and for that matter"—he glared at Kirk—"even chased out of it. Is there no rest, is there no peace, for the benevolent?"

He leaned forward earnestly. "I stand before this court, before a jury not of my peers but of artificial girls—uh, men. How can they understand my motives? They have no human hearts! 'The quality of mercy is not strained, it falleth as the gentle rain from heaven upon the place beneath; it blesseth him that gives and him that takes, becomes the throned monarch better than his crown—' But why go on? Machines, to judge a man . . ." Mudd turned, for dramatic effect, his shoulders bent, gazing upward with an expression intended as noble despair.

Kirk was aware of awe. There seemed to be no situation that Harry Mudd could not twist to his own ends. The androids were silent, puzzling over his words.

At last the judge spoke. "We must concede that the counsel for the defense has perhaps made a point of order. We may not be his peers. But among us are many who are, and the court will adjourn while a new jury including humans is sworn in. Captain Kirk, is there any let or hindrance to this?"

"Unless your law prohibits non-residents, or they are required to take any oath that interferes with their primary loyalty, I see no difficulty. But—"

"If I may interrupt, Captain?" said Spock. "The court should understand that a human jury may be swayed by many factors that have nothing to do with the legal facts of the case—the prosecutor's oratory, the atmospheric humidity, the defendant's expression—and there seem to be strong feelings about this particular defendant."

McCoy stood. "May I remind Mister Spock, who seems to feel that machine minds are more likely to offer justice, that in the ancient trial from which the defendant quoted (Shylock versus Antonio, Venice, 1504 Old Calendar) the issue was not decided by the emotional appeal—but by the letter of the law!"

Spock and McCoy glared at each other.

"Gentlemen," said the judge plaintively, "it would seem that you two are conducting a trial of us, rather than of the Human Mudd. And perhaps you are right. He has called our status as a court of law into question, and many of the crimes of which he stands accused are crimes against the person. *Are* we persons, in the eyes of Law?"

"That is to say, *in legalis homo*," explained Clarence.

"Whew!" said Yeoman Weinberg.

"That is indeed a primary question," said Spock.

"So we are in truth on trial," said the judge. "We have learned much from our contacts with you humans. We wish now to claim the right, as sentient beings, to apply for recognition as an independent planet, and membership in the Federation. Captain Kirk, can you make this decision?"

"I can only make a recommendation," said Kirk slowly. "My recommendation would carry a good deal of weight, of course."

The judge stood and threw off his scarlet robe. "Until we can wear these robes by right, we will set them aside. The trial of the Human Mudd is hereby declared in recess, and we will present our case to you and your officers, as representatives of the Federation. Pending your decision, we will then consider the case of Mudd."

Mudd watched, open-mouthed, as the jury filed from its box, and the officers of the *Enterprise* took its place.

"This is an unco thing," muttered Scott. "We start wi' a trial o' yon skillum Mudd, and end up trying the judge. Something's gone sair agley!"

"Neither life-form nor humanoid, and certainly not human," said McCoy to Kirk.

"A very special case," replied the Captain. "You may proceed."

Clarence stood before them, in a plain gray tunic. "I am authorized to state our position to you, Captain and sirs.

"We have listened to you speaking of *souls*, of *emotions*, of *mercy*, of *humanity*. We have studied these matters," he began. "Emotions can be defined as sensations of response to situations perceived, composed of biochemical effects such as blood pressure, hormone levels, nervous tone and the evocation of memory. Is that correct?"

McCoy nodded. "More or less."

"Do you dispute that we have memory?"

The *Enterprise* contingent shook its collective head. "No."

"But we have emotional memory," said McCoy. "Sometimes we remember what we felt about an event better than the event itself. In extreme cases, sometimes we don't even recognize a recorded playback."

"That is a phenomenon we cannot know," acknowledged the android. "But does an accurate memory disqualify us from membership?" Spock cocked an eyebrow at McCoy, who looked confused.

"And we can prove to you that we have analogues of the other factors of your 'emotion.' Is an electrical impulse between nerve cells inherently different from an electrical impulse between the filaments of our internal system? Your animal-based reactions cause adrenalin to flow into your blood before you can analyze whether a situation requires it; we do not increase our energies involuntarily. When confronted with a possible crisis, we analyze and *decide* whether to call up reserves of energy."

"It sounds like an advantage." said Kirk.

"It is."

"It sounds to me like hairsplitting," said Weinberg. "There are biological races with sufficient control of their bodies to do that."

Kirk acknowledged the point. Spock relaxed.

"Do you doubt that we are conscious?" continued the android.

"No. You are certainly conscious. But if one turns off your central computer, you lose consciousness," said McCoy.

"That is not exactly the case, sir; it only denies us access to our collective memory and information. Were not the Aruhus and the other androids on your ship aware, in spite of being disconnected?"

"You neither metabolize nor grow," said McCoy, hard-pressed.

"*In contraria*," said Clarence. "We metabolize pure energy. We do not grow because we are complete. We do adapt—even, as you know, to the vacuum of space without protection."

"And reproduction?"

"Because our factories are outside our bodies, which are housings, do we not reproduce?"

"Now we reach the nitty-gritty," said McCoy fiercely. "We too say our bodies are housings—for the soul."

"What is the soul, Doctor?"

"Uh. Well, that part of man that cannot be defined, analyzed, known, and which departs at death."

"That is not specific, sir."

"There you are," said McCoy. "On all other grounds, you have a case. But there . . . I don't know."

"Captain Kirk, do you have one of these?"

"I suppose I do."

"And you, sir, the Vulcan—do you?"

With delight, McCoy watched Spock turning pale green. He glared at the doctor. The prosecutor looked at Kirk. "Do we founder on this . . . *soul?*" he asked sadly.

"Sir, may I speak?" said Weinberg. Kirk nodded. "I sure can't define the soul. But these androids have done things we ought to notice. They were grateful that we rescued the Aruhus and the others. Is gratitude mechanical? They are trying Mudd for infringing their civil rights. If they respect civil rights, they value the freedom of choice. And I don't know any religion that doesn't say that a soul must choose its path. They enjoy learning—isn't joy something of the soul?

"Why did you make so many Aruhus?" he said to the prosecutor.

"She was beautiful, in mind and form," said the Clarence.

"Isn't it part of the soul's job to appreciate beauty?" said Weinberg passionately.

"I think," said McCoy, "that it may be necessary for the soul to know loneliness."

"Ah," said the android. "Is that like disconnection? Our units who returned with you have shared their sensations of separation with us. It was a new and dysfunctional experience to us, who have a collective mind."

Spock, who had been containing himself with some difficulty, rose to his feet. "Captain," he said, with a strange note in his voice, "within the United Planets there are peoples with mineral-based metabolisms; peoples who are mutually telepathic; and *some* peoples who value the higher functions of rationality. If these android people are denied the right to independent political existence, it would be illogical to retain—shall we say, the Vulcans, for instance." He tossed a folded paper into Kirk's lap and stalked out of the courtroom.

Kirk opened the paper. It was a printout of a message from Lieutenant Spxyx of the Computer Service Division. STARDATE 6067.8 SPOCK ENTERPRISE/ SABOTAGE NEGATIVE/ MARK ZX856 RECONTRACTS/ FEEDBACK OSCILLATION BREAKDOWN/

SPOCK HEAR THIS. SOLE OUTPUT/ WHO AM I/ NOW
TOTALED/ HUMAN COLLEAGUE SAYS HOPE WE HAVE
NOT COMMITTED MURDER SPXYX.

Kirk handed the paper to Mister Scott, who
read it and flushed. "I dinna ken, Captain, I
dinna ken. If I maun start thinking of machines
as people, where will it end? Telling bedtime tales
to my engines?"

"Perhaps Mister Scott is finding that illogical. When your engines begin wondering who they
are, sir, you may then have to take it under advise-
ment," said Clarence.

Scott scratched his head. "It's a muckle too phil-
osophical, and that's the truth. I'm a practical
man, Captain, but even I forget these androids
are computers got up in fancy dress. I keep talking to 'em. I'm not knowing the truth of it . . ."
A puzzled man, he followed Spock.

"So we have one vote in favor, and one ab-
stention, in effect," said Kirk. "Uhura? Sulu?
Chekov?"

In his own way, each of them said, "I don't
know." Chekov added, shamefacedly, "None of
them are likely to think they're ancient Tartars,
anyway . . ."

"Will he be all right?" Kirk asked, worriedly, as
he watched them depart.

"As long as he stays out of Barrier-impregnated
dilithium crystal range," said McCoy. "Not something likely to come up again."

"The androids who were aboard the *Superstella*
during the Barrier crossing reported internal
electrical disturbances, altered reaction times and
sensory malfunctioning," said their spokesman.

"H'm," said McCoy. "So did we."

"Well, Bones, it looks like the decision is up
to us. Do we recommend the androids of Liticia
for Federation membership or not?"

"I will leave you to talk privately," said Clarence. The room cleared. The jury box was empty,
save for the Captain and the doctor.

Behind them sounded a cough. "Sir," said Yeoman Weinberg, "I have brought a copy of the Articles of Confederation." He handed them the thick book, and added, "It doesn't say anywhere that a race has to have souls to be members." He saluted formally and departed.

Kirk looked at McCoy, and McCoy looked at Kirk, and laughter overtook them.

"Well, McCoy, I guess that does for the last objection. I admit I didn't want to refuse them—they have a lot to offer!"

"Well," said Mudd grumpily, led before the reconvened courtroom, "This is a pretty mess. I may be unusual, but nobody can question my loyalty to the human race. I refuse to take any further part in these obscene proceedings . . ." Whereupon he sat, folded his arms and elevated his nose ceilingward.

"We will proceed, gentlemen. Court is now in session."

The only surprise of the trial occurred when Yeoman Weinberg, in the part of counsel for the defense, called an android witness.

Clarence himself took the stand—once again divesting himself of his robe for the occasion.

"The defendant has, as you know, agreed to plead guilty to the tax evasion charges"—Mudd, although he did not look down, visibly flinched; Yeoman Weinberg must have been extraordinarily persuasive—"to the charges of speculation, exploitation and embezzlement"—a murmur went through the courtroom—"and sundry other charges. Indeed, he can do nothing else. However, is it the considered opinion of this witness, who is thoroughly briefed on the laws of the land, that the crimes against the person were committed during a *subjective time when the persons were legitimately to be so regarded.*" With an air of triumph, Yeoman Weinberg stepped back.

Yeoman Weinberg, thought Kirk, might, after all, go far in the Diplomatic Service. He seemed to have rather a knack for putting his finger on clinching arguments—whatever the consequences.

The witness cleared his throat. "Harumph." He pronounced this word distinctly. "My esteemed opponent has raised a point calculated to seize up the most advanced of logic circuits. Indeed, if we were to grant the point, the entire temporal basis of this trial would have to be altered, and the legal system allowed to have been in a state of *posse* rather than *esse* during the events pertaining to the crimes. The defendant, at that time, took great care to remain within the letter of the law as he understood it to exist. In that case, it would be impossible to convict the prisoner of any crime other than the piloting of his craft without a license."

Mudd, who had ignored the previous arguments, apparently lost in dreams, sat up and gazed at the android.

"A Daniel, a Daniel come to judgment!" he said. "Sweet reason prevails at last! A fine, a mere fine, and I'm free." A look of scorn was thrown at the assembled throng. "What dunderheads. I could have told you that in the first place."

"Why didn't you?" asked the judge.

Mudd shrugged. "You were having a learning experience. All you robots, I beg your pardon, mechanical persons, up until all hours every night with your precedents and interplanetary law . . ." He sat back with infinite satisfaction and put his feet up. "Thanks for the entertainment. Can we go home now?"

"There is no precedent for this case," said the judge. "Therefore, since I believe all arguments for both sides have now been heard, I charge the jury—now composed half of humans and half of androids—to withdraw and consider its verdict. The last argument of the defense, as presented by the prosecuting attorney, will be duly considered with the other evidence. Court will now recess while the jury conducts its deliberations."

The six jurymen from the *Enterprise* filed solemnly out with their android colleagues, looking perplexed.

"I hope they can disentangle this," said Kirk. "It needs more than a Daniel, it needs a Solomon!"

"Indeed, Captain," replied Spock. "This case will set a precedent for time-paradox cases. I tend to question the validity of the jury trial in such a matter."

"Well, how would you decide, Spock?" said Kirk, smiling. "Logic can't do it, not this time. And somebody has to make a decision."

"Off with his head," muttered McCoy.

"At least," said Spock, "we are spared the alternative of tyrannical *force majesté*."

The jury was out for a very long time.

When they returned to the reconvened court, the spokesman (a Marilyn) stood before them. Her rosebud lips opened.

"We find, your honor, that this case can only be considered on the basis of the time-sequence of experience. This was as follows: acts were committed by the defendant, as we have heard; the adventures within the time loop were next; the return to the Galaxy; and *then* the formation of the Government, the Constitution and the laws of Liticia. Therefore, the defendant is guilty as charged."

Mudd seemed to collapse within his velvet tunic, a broken man.

"But," went on the Marilyn, "he cannot be convicted. The only offense committed simultaneously with a law against it is—operating a ship without a license."

Mudd swelled out his clothes again. McCoy buried his head in his hands.

"The judge will now pronounce sentence," said the herald majestically. "The defendant will rise." Mudd skipped to his feet.

"Oh, all right," he said. "Another couple of

minutes of this *son-et-lumière* if you must. It does need a finale—but you can't beat the show I put on in the Magellanic Clouds with a piddling little fine."

"Silence in the court."

"It is within the powers vested in the court to determine the sentence. In view of the case of Dra-shevin versus the Licensing Board of Shere Khan, and in view of the previous two convictions for the same offense on the part of the defendant, I sentence you, Harcourt Fenton Mudd, to banishment from this planet, from all contiguous planetary space and from all planets and planetary space contiguous to any Sector within the jurisdiction of the United Federation of Planets."

Mudd looked disconcerted.

". . . under the control of the Klingon Empire . . ."

Mudd looked disturbed.

". . . or under the authority of the Romulan Empire and its allies, for ever and *in aeternum.*"

Mudd looked appalled, as the last words rolled round the room. "You can't do this to me, I'll appeal, I'll appeal to the Supreme Court—"

"The Supreme Court has given us blanket authorization to dispose of you as we see fit."

"A mandamus," said Clarence happily.

"You are a menace to the order of this Galaxy and will forthwith be removed from it. Your ship is waiting," concluded the judge.

"Sh-ship?"

"A somewhat improved version of the *Superstella,* redesigned for one-way passage through the Barrier. You will find it quite comfortable. It is even fitted with companions for you—not quite what you are used to, of course. The crew are female-shaped automata, non-conscious. Both they and the ship are irreversibly programmed to self-destruct if you make any effort to return to this Galaxy.

"We wish you a pleasant journey. Court is adjourned."

A small group watched the ship take off, ears filled with the complex and inspired cursing of Harcourt Fenton Mudd.

"That should be the last we hear of *him*," said McCoy.

They looked up at the starry sky, the constellation of the Toucan, the two Magellanic Clouds.

"I wonder," said Kirk, "since we came back in time—did the catastrophe to the Cloud occur at all?"

"We'll know that in about one hundred sixty thousand years," said Spock, "when the light of its recent past reaches us."

"By that time, he'll probably have blown up the other one," said Weinberg.

"He's just as likely to find a way to sell it," sighed Kirk.

CALENDAR

Star Dates

THE EXCITING REALM OF STAR TREK

Bantam Book Catalog

Here's your up-to-the-minute listing of every book currently available from Bantam.

This easy-to-use catalog is divided into categories and contains over 1400 titles by your favorite authors.

So don't delay—take advantage of this special opportunity to increase your reading pleasure.

Just send us your name and address and 25¢ (to help defray postage and handling costs).